REVIEWS IN ENGINEERING GEOLOGY
VOLUME XI

STORM-INDUCED GEOLOGIC HAZARDS: CASE HISTORIES FROM THE 1992–1993 WINTER IN SOUTHERN CALIFORNIA AND ARIZONA

Edited by

ROBERT A. LARSON
Los Angeles County
Department of Public Works
900 South Fremont Avenue
Alhambra, California 91803

and

JAMES E. SLOSSON
Slosson and Associates
15500 Erwin Street, Suite 1123
Van Nuys, California 91411

The Geological Society of America, Inc.
3300 Penrose Place, P.O. Box 9140
Boulder, Colorado 80301
1997

The Reviews in Engineering Geology series was expanded in 1997 to include Engineering Geology Case Histories, 11 volumes of which were published by the Geological Society of America from 1957 to 1978 with ISBNs from 0-8137-4001-0 to 0-8137-4011-8. Beginning with this volume, Reviews in Engineering Geology may include both reviews and case histories, under the ISBN 0-8137-4111-4 and subsequent numbers.

Published by The Geological Society of America, Inc.
3300 Penrose Place, P.O. Box 9140, Boulder, Colorado 80301

Printed in U.S.A.

GSA Books Science Editor Abhijit Basu

Library of Congress Cataloging-in-Publication Data
Storm-induced geologic hazards : case histories from the 1992-1993
    winter in southern California and Arizona / edited by Robert A.
    Larson and James E. Slosson.
        p.   cm. -- (Reviews in engineering geology ; v. 11)
        Includes bibliographical references and index.
        ISBN 0-8137-4111-4
        1. Landslides--California.   2. Landslides--Arizona.   3. Floods-
    -California.   4. Floods--Arizona.   5. Storms--California.
    6. Storms--Arizona.   I. Larson, Robert A., 1956-   . II. Slosson,
    James E., 1923-   . III. Series.
    TA705.R4 vol. 11
    [QE599.U5]
    624.1'51 s--dc21   97-26969
    [363.34'92'09794]   CIP

10 9 8 7 6 5 4 3 2 1

Contents

Foreword

The Engineering Geology Division of the Geological Society of America is proud to celebrate our 50th anniversary year with the release of this volume.

The Engineering Geology division of GSA was founded in 1947 as the first topical group within the Society. One of the first major activities of the new division was to prepare a special commemorative volume, in honor of Charles Berkey, entitled *The Application of Geology to Engineering Practice*. The resulting Berkey volume was printed and reprinted six times between 1950 and 1967.

Preparation of publications on various aspects of engineering geology has continued to be one of the division's most important activities. The *Engineering Geology Case Histories* series was initiated in 1957 to show how geology affects the planning, design, construction, and maintenance or operation of engineering works. In 11 volumes, the division and the Society documented conditions and problems related to tunnels, dams, landslides, river diversions, ground water, waste disposal, foundation performance, mine subsidence, swelling soils, man-induced seismicity, effects of rapid excavation, geologic mapping, behavior of stone as a construction material, and legal aspects of practicing geology.

Shortly after the Case Histories series was launched, the need was recognized for a different style of publication, which presented review articles on major topics in engineering geology. The first volume of *Reviews in Engineering Geology* was released in 1962. Nine others have followed.

The need for information on applied geology continues. Engineering geology has long relied on the study of case histories to provide exposure to the real-world problems critical to developing the practical understanding needed to apply more general theoretical knowledge. We must continue to analyze both successful and failed projects and to publish our conclusions. We also must continue to compile and publish review articles that consolidate and summarize the rapidly increasing knowledge necessary for responsibly applying geology to engineering practice.

In our 50th anniversary year, we will formalize a trend that has been occurring for some time. Although we publish both case histories and reviews, the lines between these types of publications have become blurred. Maintaining two separate series of publications no longer seems appropriate. This volume was originally planned as Engineering Geology Case Histories Number 12. Instead it marks the beginning of the consolidation of the Case Histories and Reviews in Engineering Geology series under the single series *Reviews in Engineering Geology*.

By any name this volume is a useful addition to the literature of engineering geology. It is an appropriate publication to commemorate the Engineering Geology Division's first 50 years and to mark the beginning of our next 50 years. Let it also serve as encouragement for all engineering geologists to continue the tradition of sharing the results of their work and practical experience for the benefit of other geologists and society.

Helen L. Delano
Chair, Engineering Geology Division

Preface

In 1994, a symposium on the 1992–1993 winter storms in California and Arizona was convened at the Cordilleran Section Meeting of the Geological Society of America. Twenty-six papers were presented in a day and a half. This volume is an outgrowth of that symposium. Engineering geologists, geomorphologists, and geotechnical and hydraulic engineers have written these case histories that discuss their professional work related to the winter storms.

The episodic and catastrophic damage caused by winter storms is a growing concern of the public, insurers, and policymakers at various levels of government. The cost of damages has increased dramatically as the pace of urbanization has intensified. Society is just beginning to realize the problems created by building in geologically sensitive areas during the last 50 years—a period of postwar construction supported by a misconception that engineering technology can overcome all environmental constraints and geological instabilities.

Although this volume does not document all types of geologic hazards caused by winter storms, we hope that readers are enlightened by the real-world problems addressed in these chapters. Geologists and engineers can and must learn from past examples if they are to succeed in reducing the economic, political, social, and emotional costs to the public. The economic costs in particular can be traumatic to the property owner who has little hope of recovery when insurance is unavailable, such as for landslide-related losses.

The first chapter sets the stage by showing why severe winter storms occur and how they affect watersheds. The 1992–1993 winter storms and resulting floods are placed into the context of the geological record. The next two chapters, respectively, deal with problems of infrastructure construction and maintenance and mining in river channels. The fourth chapter documents ground settlement intensified by rising groundwater caused by infiltrating rain, and briefly describes the resulting litigation. The fifth and sixth chapters discuss warning the public about the hazard of imminent debris flow and how to set the moisture and rainfall thresholds that can be used to issue warnings. The effects of rainfall-activated landslides that damaged homes in southern California are covered in the last two chapters.

This volume marks a change in content for the Reviews in Engineering Geology series. Now both case histories, published separately by the Geological Society of America between 1957 and 1978, and review papers may be presented within this single series. Our intent with this volume, as with the original case histories series, is to aid practicing geologists and engineers. We also hope that those students and teachers who want to come to grips with real-world problems not commonly presented in textbooks will also benefit from the practical knowledge presented in these chapters.

Robert A. Larson
James E. Slosson
Van Nuys, California
April 1997

Peer Reviewers

The thoughtful and insightful comments of these reviewers substantially improved this volume.

Herbert G. Adams
California State University, Northridge

William R. Adams, Jr.
Department of Transportation
Commonwealth of Pennsylvania

Peter M. Allen
Baylor University

Kim M. Bishop
California State University, Los Angeles

Koll Y. Buer
California Department of Water Resources

Scott F. Burns
Portland State University

William Cotton
William Cotton and Associates

Vincent S. Cronin
The University of Wisconsin—Milwaukee

Jerome Degraff
USDA Forest Service

Joan Florsheim
Phillip Williams and Associates, Ltd.

John R. Giardino
Texas A&M University

Douglas L. Hamilton
Irvine, California

Edwin L. Harp
United States Geological Survey

Michael W. Hart
San Diego, California

Thomas L. Holzer
United States Geological Survey

Gary Huckleberry
Arizona Geological Survey

Randall W. Jibson
United States Geological Survey

Jeffrey R. Keaton
AGRA Earth & Environmental, Inc.

G. Mathias Kondolf
University of California at Berkeley

Sree Kumar
Los Angeles County Department of Public Works

Dorian Kuper
David J. Newton and Associates

Robert C. MacArthur
Northwest Hydraulic Consultants, Inc.

Christopher C. Mathewson
Texas A&M University

Kenneth L. Meyers
WEST-TEC

Hasan Nouri
Rivertech, Inc.

Daniel D. Overton
Shepherd Miller, Inc.

Roy J. Shlemon
Roy J. Shlemon and Associates, Inc.

Gerard Shuirman
Westlake Village, California

Steve Slaff
Tucson, Arizona

Terry R. West
Purdue University

Delmar D. Yoakum
GeoSoils, Inc.

Geological Society of America
Reviews in Engineering Geology, Volume XI
1997

Hydroclimatological and paleohydrological context of extreme winter flooding in Arizona, 1993

P. Kyle House
Quaternary Sciences Center, Desert Research Institute, 7010 Dandini Boulevard, Reno, Nevada 89512
Katherine K. Hirschboeck
Laboratory of Tree-Ring Research, University of Arizona, Tucson, Arizona 85721

ABSTRACT

Extreme flooding in Arizona during the winter of 1993 resulted from a nearly optimal combination of flood-enhancing factors involving hydroclimatology, hydrometeorology, and physiography. The floods of January and February 1993 were the result of record precipitation from the passage of an unusually high number of winter storm fronts. These fronts moved across Arizona as part of an exceptionally active storm track that was located unusually far south. The number of individual storms that entered the region and the relative position of each storm track in relation to previous storms was reflected in a complex spatial and temporal distribution of flood peaks. An analysis of the hydroclimatic context of these floods supports a general conclusion that in Arizona, front-generated winter precipitation is most often the cause of extreme floods in large watersheds, even in basins that tend to experience their greatest frequency of flooding from other types of storms. A comparison of the 1993 floods with gauged, historical, and paleoflood data from Arizona indicates that, although many individual flood peaks were quite large, they were within the range of documented extreme flooding over the past 1,000+ yr. The 1993 flood scenario provides a convincing analogue for the climatic and hydrologic processes that must have operated to generate comparably large paleofloods, that is, abnormally high rainfall totals, repeated accumulation and melting of snow, and rain on snow. Such conditions are initiated and perpetuated by a persistent winter circulation anomaly in the North Pacific Ocean that repeatedly steers alternately warm and cold storms into the region along a southerly displaced storm track. This scenario is enhanced by an active subtropical jet stream, common during El Niño–Southern Oscillation periods.

INTRODUCTION

Record flood peaks occurred in many watersheds in Arizona during January and February 1993 (Smith et al., 1994). This widespread, high-magnitude flooding was the culmination of record amounts of precipitation (rain and snow) that fell statewide from a long succession of storms that began in early December 1992. Approximately 16 separate storms passed over the state over a three-month period that was characterized by anomalous and persistent patterns of atmospheric circulation

(House, 1993; National Oceanic and Atmospheric Administration, 1992, 1993a, 1993b).

The 1993 flood sequence ranks as one of the most severe winter flooding episodes in Arizona history, possibly surpassed only by a similar episode in February 1891 (Patterson and Somers, 1966). In January and February 1993, record peak discharges were recorded at more than 35 stations (Fig. 1; Table 1). Unprecedented flow volumes and durations occurred, causing great concern for floodplain and reservoir management (Fig. 2). On several occasions in 1993, large volumes of inflow overtaxed reservoirs and

House, P. K., and Hirschboeck, K. K., 1997, Hydroclimatological and paleohydrological context of extreme winter flooding in Arizona, 1993, *in* Larson, R. A., and Slosson, J. E., eds., Storm-Induced Geologic Hazards: Case Histories from the 1992–1993 Winter in Southern California and Arizona: Boulder, Colorado, Geological Society of America Reviews in Engineering Geology, v. XI.

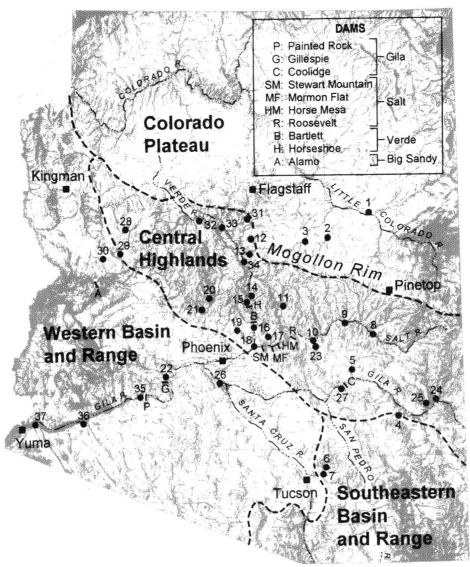

Figure 1. Map of Arizona showing physiographic regions discussed in text, sites of record floods at stations with at least 10 yr of record (numbered), the location of dams affected by flooding, and the location of sites mentioned in the text. Each record flood site is listed and described in Table 1.

forced massive, dramatic releases of flood runoff from many dams in Arizona (Fig. 3). The protracted flow durations downstream from the dams enhanced severe erosion of some floodplain areas. On the middle Gila River, for example, it has been shown that the protracted flow duration caused considerably greater channel and floodplain erosion than did a previous, shorter-lived flood with a greater instantaneous peak discharge (Huckleberry, 1994). The floodplain and channel erosion problem along much of the length of the Gila River during 1993 was probably compounded by sustained releases from flood control structures.

Total estimated damage from the 1993 floods exceeded $400 million, and total federal expenditures related to the flooding exceeded $220 million (U.S. Army Corps of Engineers, 1994). The Red Cross reported eight deaths and 112 injuries related to the floods. Federal disaster declarations were issued for 13 of 15 counties in Arizona, a direct reflection of the regional scope and severity of the flooding.

The goal of this chapter is to describe the 1993 Arizona flood sequence in the large-scale and long-term context of its hydroclimatic and hydrometeorologic origins and historical/prehistoric forerunners. In illustrating some of the more interesting flood phenomena, specific examples are presented that are assumed to have been reasonably representative of conditions throughout Arizona during the winter of 1992–1993.

THE CAUSES OF FLOODING

Flooding results from the interaction of three factors: (1) the short-term precipitation-delivering mechanisms that are the most immediate cause of the excessive runoff (*flood hydrometeorology*), (2) the large-scale atmospheric circulation pat-

TABLE 1. SUMMARY OF RECORD DISCHARGES IN ARIZONA, JANUARY AND FEBRUARY 1993*

Point	Site	USGS Number	Area (km²)	Peak Discharge (m³s⁻¹)	Date 1993	Record Length	Prior Flood of Record Peak Discharge (m³s⁻¹)	Prior Flood of Record Date
1	Leroux Wash near Holbrook, AZ	9397100	2,095	240	8-Jan	13	215	24-Aug-92
2	Chevelon Creek near Winslow, AZ	9397500	702	699	8-Jan	35§	564	18-Dec-78
3	Clear Creek near Winslow, AZ†	9398500	821	824	8-Jan	42	558	18-Dec-78
4	Frye Creek near Thatcher, AZ	9460150	10	14	8-Jan	17§	3	24-Aug-92
5	San Carlos River near Peridot, AZ	9468500	2,657	1,552	8-Jan	68§	1,150	14-Mar-41
6	Sabino Creek near Tucson, AZ	9484000	92	365	8-Jan	63§	219	6-Sep-70
7	Tanque Verde Creek near Tucson, AZ	9484500	567	694	8-Jan	27§	360	18-Dec-78
8	Black River near Fort Apache, AZ	9490500	3,191	1,549	8-Jan	45§	1,252	2-Oct-83
9	Salt River near Chrysotile, AZ	9497500	7,379	2,169	8-Jan	71	1,994	18-Dec-78
10	Salt River near Roosevelt, AZ	9498500	11,153	4,050	8-Jan	82	3,313	14-Mar-41
11	Tonto Creek near Roosevelt, AZ	9499000	1,748	2,053	8-Jan	55	1,739	15-Feb-80
12	Wet Beaver Creek near Rimrock, AZ	9505200	287	453	8-Jan	34	309	19-Feb-80
13	West Clear Creek near Camp Verde, AZ	9505800	624	702	8-Jan	30	634	18-Dec-78
14	Wet Bottom Creek near Childs, AZ	9508300	94	209	8-Jan	28	193	19-Feb-80
15	Verde River below Tangle Creek, AZ	9508500	14,227	4,106	8-Jan	50	2,684	15-Feb-80
16	Verde River below Bartlett Dam, AZ†	9510000	15,032	3,115	8-Jan	56	2,860	2-Mar-78
17	Rock Creek near Sunflower, AZ	9510180	39	72	8-Jan	12§	54	22-Dec-65
18	Verde River near Scottsdale, AZ†	9511300	16,188	3,597	8-Jan	34	2,775	16-Feb-80
19	Cave Creek near Cave Creek, AZ	9512280	214	261	8-Jan	15	110	1-Mar-91
20	Boulder Creek near Rock Springs, AZ	9512830	98	283	8-Jan	10	91	1-Mar-91
21	Humbug Creek near Castle Hot Springs, AZ	9512860	155	170	8-Jan	12	91	1-Mar-91
22	Gila River at Gillespie Dam, AZ†	9518000	128,594	3,682	9-Jan	54	3,511	17-Feb-80
23	Pinal Creek near Globe, AZ	9498400	420	161	11-Jan	15	83	9-Jul-81
24	Eagle Creek near Morenci, AZ†	9447000	1,611	1,042	18-Jan	51	1,031	2-Oct-83
25	Bonita Creek near Morenci, AZ	9447800	782	552	18-Jan	14	549	2-Oct-83
26	Gila River near Laveen, AZ†	9479500	53,393	1,178	20-Jan	54	991	4-Oct-83
27	Gila River below Coolidge Dam, AZ†	9469500	33,375	830	21-Jan	67	142	6-Oct-83
28	Francis Creek near Bagdad, AZ	9424432	347	354	8-Feb	10	193	25-Aug-88
29	Burro Creek near Bagdad, AZ	9424447	1,557	1,566	8-Feb	14	866	3-Mar-83
30	Big Sandy River near Wikieup, AZ	9424450	7,076	1,946	8-Feb	29	1,090	20-Feb-80
31	Oak Creek at Sedona, AZ	9504430	603	657	19-Feb	14	586	12-Mar-82
32	Verde River near Paulden, AZ	9503700	5,569	657	20-Feb	32	445	20-Feb-80
33	Verde River near Clarkdale, AZ	9504000	8.130	1.507	20-Feb	35	1,433	21-Feb-80
34	Verde River near Camp Verde, AZ	9506000	12,028	3,370	20-Feb	18§	2,747	3-Mar-38
35	Gila River below Painted Rock Dam, AZ†	9519800	131,857	906	26-Feb	36	260	3-May-83
36	Gila River near Mohawk, AZ†	9520360	143,564	773	1-Mar	20	121	20-Apr-80
37	Gila River near Dome, AZ†	9520500	149,832	818	3-Mar	36	136	18-Sep-63

*Only stations with more than 10 years of record are shown. Data from Smith et al., 1994.
†Drainage regulated above station. Period of record corresponds to period of affected flow.
§Period of record is not continuous.

terns and antecedent seasonal precipitation conditions prior to and during the flood (*flood hydroclimatology*), and (3) the *physiography*, that is, the drainage basin characteristics of the stream systems that must accommodate the excessive runoff.

Flood hydrometeorology focuses on the sequence of local weather events occurring over minutes, hours, and days that are the most immediate—or proximate—causes of flooding. These short-term, local-scale meteorological events emerge from a longer-term (weeks, months, seasons, years) and larger-scale (regional, hemispheric, global) context that has been defined as "flood hydroclimatology" (Hirschboeck, 1988). Flood hydroclimatology places regional hydrometeorologic flooding activity in the context of its history of variation over a longer period of time that includes preceding weeks, months, seasons, and years. It also

examines the uniqueness of flooding events in terms of their antecedent conditions and the spatial framework of the regional and global network of changing combinations of meteorological elements such as storm tracks, air masses, pressure-height anomalies, and other components of the large-scale circulation. Consideration of floods in their hydroclimatological context allows individual flood events to be linked to atmospheric phenomena operating at longer time scales and global spatial scales. Physiography is the terrestrial component of the three factors that generate floods. We use the term physiography to refer to all physical aspects of a drainage basin: topography (e.g., elevation distribution, relief, drainage density, basin shape), vegetation, land use, soil characteristics, and geology. These are the factors that influence the storage, distribution, and ultimate concentration of

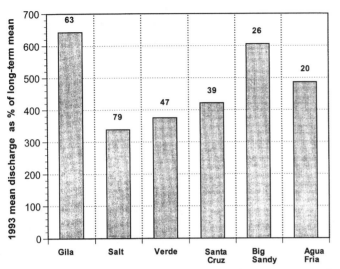

Figure 2. 1993 mean annual discharge expressed as a percentage of the long-term mean for selected, unregulated streams in Arizona. Numbers above the bars correspond to the length of record (years) on which the long-term mean is based. Data from Smith et al. (1994).

Figure 3. Photographs of two major dams in Arizona adversely affected by flooding during the winter of 1993. Upper photo, Roosevelt Dam on the Salt River, January 19, 1993. Lower photo, Coolidge Dam on the Gila River, January 16, 1993. Photographs provided by the U.S. Bureau of Reclamation.

atmospheric moisture into runoff. Basin physiography is the component that integrates precipitation from discrete weather events, which are embedded in the larger-scale circulation features, into flood peaks, flood volumes, and flow durations.

FLOODING IN ARIZONA—PHYSIOGRAPHY, CLIMATOLOGY, AND DRAINAGE

The physiography and climatology of Arizona provide the framework for a spatially and temporally diverse flooding regime. In order to place the Arizona floods of 1993 in context, first we will provide an overview of the physiographic and climatic setting in which the floods developed. In the following sections the discussions of the climatology of Arizona are derived from Sellers and Hill (1974), Hirschboeck (1985, 1987), Webb and Betancourt (1992), and Ely (1992).

Basin and Range Province

Arizona comprises three distinctive physiographic provinces: the Basin and Range, Colorado Plateau, and Central Highlands (Fig. 1). The western, south-central, and southeastern parts of Arizona make up the Basin and Range Province. It is characterized by widely spaced mountain ranges of relatively limited extent separated by wide, low-lying alluvial valleys. The highest mountains in the province are located in the southeastern portion where elevations in excess of 2,740 m (9,000 ft) are common. Maximum elevations rarely exceed 1,525 m (5,000 ft) in the western portion.

The climate of the Basin and Range Province varies from arid in the west to semiarid in the southeast. Rainfall in the region is characterized by a distinct bimodal seasonality with a precipitation maximum in summer and a secondary maximum in winter. Overall, rainfall totals are highest in the southeast because of a greater orographic influence than exists in the western portion. Most streams in the Basin and Range Province are

ephemeral. Some streams with perennial reaches occur in the southeastern portion.

Summer precipitation and occasional flash flooding occur in the Basin and Range Province as a result of intense convectional thunderstorms during seasonal influxes of atmospheric moisture from the Pacific Ocean, the Gulf of California, or humid regions of tropical Mexico. In some years the summer precipitation season is enhanced or prolonged into fall by rainfall associated with excess moisture from tropical storms in the eastern North Pacific Ocean or Gulf of California. Winter precipitation is primarily associated with passing fronts. Some frontal storms are associated with warmer, subtropical atmospheric flow and yield only rainfall. Others are southerly displaced cold fronts that deliver rainfall to the valleys and snow to the upper elevations, except in the western portion where snowfall is rare. Winter snow accumulation and subsequent melting are not major sources of flood runoff in the Basin and Range Province in Arizona except locally in the southeastern portion.

Central Highlands Province

The Central Highlands Province has very rugged topography characterized by closely spaced mountain ranges and deep canyons. Elevations range from around 305 m (1,000 ft) to about 2,740 m (9,000 ft) on the highest peaks. The orientation of the rugged Central Highlands Province is roughly northwest-southeast, thus presenting a prominent orographic barrier to storms coming in from the southwest across the low desert. The Central Highlands Province is separated from the considerably less rugged Colorado Plateau by the Mogollon Rim, which is a distinct erosional escarpment along most of its length. The southwest face of the rim is dissected by deeply incised canyons that flow through the Central Highlands toward the south and west.

Like the Basin and Range Province to the south, the precipitation regime in the Central Highlands Province has a distinct bimodal seasonality. However, larger winter precipitation totals (rain and snow) occur because of a higher frequency of winter frontal storm passages and a more pronounced orographic effect. Summer precipitation totals are also somewhat higher and result from more frequent, orographically enhanced, convective storm activity and occasional influxes of moisture from Pacific tropical storms.

Many streams draining the Central Highlands and Mogollon Rim maintain perennial flow as a result of a precipitation-enhancing orographic effect that activates summer convectional showers and fosters the accumulation of snow from winter frontal storms. In the larger drainage basins, substantial snow accumulations can have an important effect on winter and spring flooding. Snowmelt runoff and rain falling on snow are much more likely to generate flood runoff here than in the Basin and Range Province to the south.

Colorado Plateau Province

The Colorado Plateau Province is a relatively low-relief, sparsely vegetated, high-elevation part of north-northeastern Arizona, with widely spaced mesas, buttes, and small, isolated mountain ranges. It exhibits the same bimodal precipitation regime as the Central Highlands Province to the south but has lower overall precipitation totals, especially in winter. This difference is due to the lack of a significant orographic influence, the effect of downslope adiabatic drying, and a greater distance from oceanic moisture sources. Most streams in this northern part of the state flow in response to local convectional thunderstorms in summer and precipitation from frequent frontal storms in winter. Occasionally in summer and fall, tropical storms provide a source of excess atmospheric moisture even as far north as the Colorado Plateau.

Major drainages in Arizona

The two largest river basins in Arizona are the Gila River Basin and the Lower Colorado River Basin (above the confluence of the Colorado River and the Gila River in western Ari-

zona). The Gila River Basin includes most streams in the Basin and Range Province and most streams in the Central Highlands Province that drain toward the south away from the Mogollon Rim. The Lower Colorado River Basin includes much of the Colorado Plateau Province and is dominated by the Colorado and Little Colorado Rivers. Other tributary source areas in the Lower Colorado River Basin include a lesser portion of the Central Highland Province and extensive desert areas in the western Basin and Range Province.

Within the Gila River Basin, the Santa Cruz and San Pedro Rivers are the major systems draining the southeastern Basin and Range Province. They flow northward from source regions in Mexico (San Pedro River) and along the Arizona-Mexico border (Santa Cruz River). Some of their tributaries originate in the high elevations of the southeastern mountain ranges, but most of the drainage area in the Santa Cruz and San Pedro River Basins is below 1,220 m (4,000 ft).

The northern half of the Gila River Basin is dominated by the Salt and Verde Rivers. The entire basin of the Salt River is in the Central Highlands region, and many of its tributaries originate on the southern face of the Mogollon Rim. The headwaters of the Verde River are on the Colorado Plateau, but the majority of the basin is also within the Central Highlands Province. Most of the Verde River's major tributaries flow in canyons that are deeply incised into the Mogollon Rim. Both the Salt and Verde River Basins have large portions of their drainage areas above 1,830 m (6,000 ft).

The lower reaches of the Salt and Verde Rivers are extensively regulated for flood control, irrigation, and municipal water supply (Fig. 1). The rivers join east of Phoenix, where the name Salt River is retained for the trunk stream. Just west of Phoenix, the Salt River joins the Gila River. The Gila is the master drainage, ultimately draining 148,864 km^2 (57,477 mi^2). This is more than 50% of the total area of Arizona. The lower Gila River is also extensively regulated. It traverses the southern half of Arizona in an east-west direction and joins the Colorado River at Yuma, Arizona.

Hydroclimatic flooding regimes of Arizona

The interaction between seasonal climate and physiography in different regions of Arizona results in interesting contrasts in the flooding regimes of the major drainages. Because of distinctive combinations of the climatic processes involved in the generation of floods in Arizona—that is, frontal rainfall, convectional thunderstorm rainfall, tropical storm rainfall, and snowmelt—flood records from most Arizona stream gauges can be decomposed into hydroclimatically defined mixed distributions (Hirschboeck, 1985, 1987). This is an effective method for exploring the underlying hydroclimatic causes for individual events in a gauged flood record and for better evaluating the kinds of hydroclimatic conditions that are likely to generate the most extreme events, such as the floods of 1993.

To illustrate this "flood hydroclimatology" approach, Figures 4a and 4b depict the hydroclimatically decomposed flood records for the Santa Cruz River at Tucson (USGS gauge no. 09482500; Fig. 4a), a drainage basin representative of the southeastern Basin and Range Province, and the Verde River below Tangle Creek (USGS gauge no. 09508500; Fig. 4b), a basin located principally in the Central Highlands Province. The discharges are presented in the form of standardized dimensionless z scores for easier comparison (Hirschboeck, 1985, 1987). The complete histogram of all peaks-above-base during the period 1950 through 1985 is shown for each stream on the left of Figure 4, with the largest annual flood peaks distinguished from other peaks greater than the station's base discharge (partial duration peaks). To the right of each stream's complete histogram, the same peaks have been regrouped into separate subgroup histograms according to what type of climatic process generated each flood: tropical storm rainfall, convectional rainfall, or frontal precipitation (rain and/or snow). The 1993 peaks have been plotted for each stream for comparison with the 1950–1985 gauged record.

This methodology shows that summer flooding as a result of convectional rainfall is more frequent in the southeastern Basin and Range Province, whereas winter flooding as a result of frontal storms and snowmelt is more common in the Central Highlands Province. This variation comes from geographic and physiographic influences on the types and frequencies of synoptic meteorological events. Although winter frontal precipitation can occur throughout Arizona, the influence of fronts is greater in the Central Highlands Province than in the Basin and Range Province to the south. The Central Highlands lie closer to the typical winter storm tracks that steer fronts across the western United States. Thus, the latitude of the Central Highlands Province, coupled with its orographic effect, leads to a higher frequency of floods from winter frontal precipitation (rain and snow) than is observed in the Basin and Range Province to the south.

Winter frontal storms produce floods in streams throughout much of Arizona, but the relative magnitude and frequency of these events are influenced by basin-specific physiographic characteristics. For the two basins compared in Figure 4, the Verde Basin has a larger contributing drainage area than that of the Santa Cruz Basin: 14,227 km^2 (5,493 mi^2) versus 5,755 km^2 (2,222 mi^2). The Verde River's larger drainage area influences the number and size of front-generated floods, because as basin area increases, the importance of intense convectional showers as primary flood-producing events tends to decrease. The dominance of frontal flooding in the Verde Basin is also influenced by the percentage of the basin at high elevations, where snow accumulation and subsequent melting contribute to the runoff. Thirty percent of the Verde River's drainage area is above 1,830 m (6,000 ft), whereas only 1.8% of the Santa Cruz River's drainage area is above this elevation (Hirschboeck, 1985).

Decomposition of the flood series into hydroclimatic subgroups yields information about the causes of the largest peaks in a stream's gauge record (Fig. 4). For the Verde River, the largest floods in the extreme upper tail of the histogram distribution (including the 1993 floods) are associated with the Verde

River's most common flood-generating climatic mechanism: frontal precipitation (Fig. 4b). In addition, tropical storm–related precipitation events, although rare, play a role in generating floods significantly greater than the mean. In the Santa Cruz Basin to the south, floods are most likely to be generated by summer convectional rainfall. In contrast to the Verde River, however, most of the floods in the extreme upper tail of the Santa Cruz River's flood histogram were not generated by its most common flood-generating climatic mechanism. Instead the largest discharges resulted either from tropical storm events, such as the peak of record in October 1983 (Roeske et al., 1989), or from winter frontal events such as the 1993 floods (Fig. 4a). Differences between the relative magnitudes of floods from these two storm types in the Santa Cruz and Verde River Basins probably reflect the greater likelihood of a larger snowmelt contribution to winter flooding in the Verde River Basin.

The extreme nature of the 1993 floods is underscored by evaluating them within the overall hydroclimatic context of flooding in Arizona. Hydroclimatic analysis of flood series for other Arizona streams indicates that winter frontal events are most likely to generate the largest floods in large basins of the Central Highlands Province of Arizona (Hirschboeck, 1985, 1987; Ely, 1992; Ely et al., 1994). The events of winter 1993 clearly support this. However, even in southern Arizona, which tends to be dominated by flooding from summer convectional thunderstorms or infrequent tropical storms, the 1993 winter floods were comparable to the largest floods on record.

THE 1993 ARIZONA FLOODS

The floods of January and February 1993 were the result of record precipitation from the passage of an unusually high number of winter storm fronts. These fronts moved across Arizona as part of an active storm track that was located anomalously far to the south. Frontal precipitation was frequent and heavy throughout the Central Highlands and southeastern Basin and Range Provinces from December 1992 through February 1993. Many meteorological stations in central Arizona recorded precipitation totals more than 400% of normal in January alone (MacNish et al., 1993); furthermore, it has been suggested that recurrence intervals for some of the highest precipitation totals in central Arizona during January and February 1993 were greater than 100 yr and may have been between 500 and 1,000 yr (Guttman et al., 1993). The extreme and prolonged precipitation resulted in a significant regional flooding episode in which record floods were recorded statewide (Fig. 1; Table 1). The flood source areas were limited primarily to the Central Highlands the southeastern Basin and Range, and a small portion of the Colorado Plateau, but the impact of flooding was far reaching because major drainages from these source areas traverse large portions of the state.

What combination of factors led to this major flooding event? How unusual was it within the context of the long-term climatic history and paleohydrology of flooding in Arizona? How likely is it for a similar event to occur in the future, given the uncertainty of either a naturally fluctuating or radically

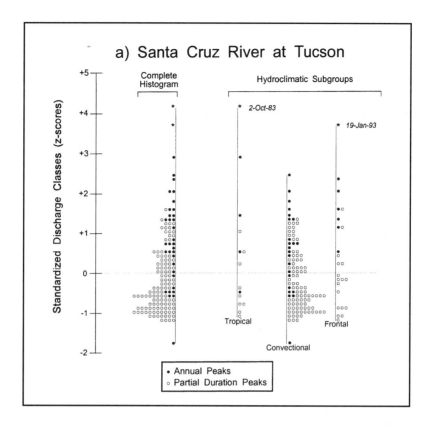

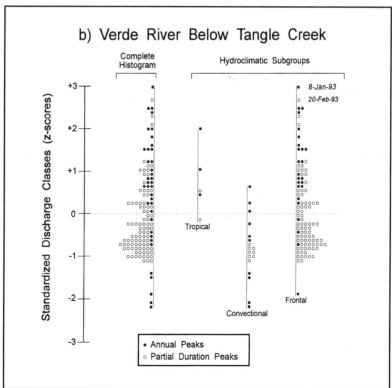

Figure 4. Decomposition of flood series from two gauging stations in Arizona according to hydroclimatic cause of flood. a, Santa Cruz River near Tucson; b, Verde River below Tangle Creek.

changing climate? We will examine these questions by presenting a detailed analysis of the hydroclimatic and physical aspects of the 1993 floods and then evaluating this information within the context of paleoflood evidence, regional historical peaks, and probable future climatic scenarios.

Atmospheric circulation features and related antecedent conditions

The hydrometeorological and hydroclimatological factors that led to the 1993 Arizona floods emerged from a series of global, hemispheric, and regional-scale climatic events. Global oceanic and atmospheric teleconnections related to El Niño–Southern Oscillation (ENSO) conditions influenced the development of large-scale atmospheric circulation anomalies in the eastern North Pacific Ocean. These anomalies were instrumental in developing flood-enhancing antecedent hydrologic conditions and in delivering precipitation that generated a sequence of large floods throughout the region.

El Niño–Southern Oscillation influences. An unusually strong, large-scale atmospheric circulation anomaly developed in the extratropical latitudes of the eastern Pacific Ocean and persisted in various forms throughout the winter of 1992–1993. During the previous winter of 1991–1992, El Niño conditions had persisted with above-normal sea-surface temperatures (SSTs) in the central and eastern tropical Pacific Ocean (Bell and Basist, 1994). By mid-1992 the index that characterizes the strength of the El Niño air-sea interaction had returned to normal, although SSTs remained above normal in the western tropical Pacific (Bell and Basist, 1994). During December 1992 and continuing through February 1993, above-normal SSTs again expanded eastward in the tropical and subtropical Pacific Ocean, and ENSO conditions redeveloped. Although not as strong as the previous winter's El Niño, winter 1992–1993 marked one of the longest periods of continuous warm SSTs on record for the tropical Pacific (Bell and Basist, 1994). The atmospheric circulation accompanying this SST anomaly was an enhanced subtropical jet stream that conveyed warm, moisture-laden air from the central equatorial Pacific to the southwestern United States.

Atmospheric circulation anomalies. Beginning in December 1992, an anomalous high-pressure area developed in the extratropical latitudes in the eastern North Pacific Ocean and persisted throughout the winter in varying degrees. This high-pressure blocking pattern over the Gulf of Alaska displaced one branch of the polar jet stream and associated Pacific storm track far to the north and another branch to the south. The southern branch combined with the enhanced subtropical jet stream. This split-flow configuration in the upper-level westerly flow led to above-normal extratropical cyclonic storm activity moving into the western United States unusually far to the south.

The anomalous and persistent atmospheric circulation patterns in January and February are depicted in Figures 5a and 5b. The broad, lightly shaded arrows indicate the mean trajectories of the two branches of the split westerly flow at the 500-mb pressure

height (roughly 5 to 6 km [3 to 4 mi] above sea level). The unusual nature of the circulation pattern in each month is revealed by the standardized anomaly contours that show how much higher or lower than normal the 500-mb pressure heights were in each month. The anomaly maps illustrate the atmospheric flow into the western United States, counterclockwise around the eastern Pacific trough (low-pressure anomaly center) just west of California and clockwise around the blocking ridge (high-pressure anomaly center) in the Gulf of Alaska. Also shown are the amount and trajectory of anomalous moisture delivery into the southwestern United States (in grams of water vapor/kilograms air/second) at low levels (850-mb height; usually below 1 to 2 km [0.6 to 1.2 mi] above sea level). In both January and February, the low-level atmospheric flow that transported this excess moisture generally followed the anomalous steering currents associated with the deep trough at the 500-mb level. December's circulation displayed a tendency toward a split-flow pattern with an anomalous trough in the eastern North Pacific west of California and a blocking ridge in the vicinity of the Gulf of Alaska. Although in December the transport of moisture into the southwestern United States at low levels was not significantly above normal, the high frequency of frontal storms that traversed the southwest that month resulted in greater than normal precipitation amounts (Bell and Basist, 1994).

The persistence of this large-scale circulation anomaly throughout the winter and the frequent recurrence of the split westerly flow configuration had a direct effect on both the individual storms that delivered flood-producing precipitation to Arizona and the antecedent conditions that evolved over time within individual drainage basins. The net result was to make the basins more and more susceptible to flooding as the winter progressed. Depending on the configuration of the daily circulation, frontal passages during December 1992 through February 1993 were associated with either cold or warm storms. During cold fronts, precipitation at the higher elevations accumulated as snow, but when an intervening warm front passed through, the warmer temperatures would instigate snowmelt, and any precipitation associated with the frontal storm would accelerate the melting process as a result of rain falling on the snow. This process repeated itself several times over the three month period.

Antecedent conditions: The importance of rain on snow. The persistence of the circulation anomaly in the eastern North Pacific Ocean and its unusually placed storm track was the ultimate cause of the severity of the winter flooding in Arizona, primarily because of its influence on two key hydrologic factors related to antecedent conditions: (1) soil moisture storage capacity and (2) snowmelt, especially in the Central Highlands region. In the first case, the unusual circulation delivered a long succession of storms that led to progressive saturation of the drainage basins such that eventually soil moisture storage capacities were exceeded in all catchments. Precipitation delivered by storms later in the season therefore immediately generated surface runoff. In the second case, shifts in the trajectory of the storm track across Arizona and its southward displacement resulted in alter-

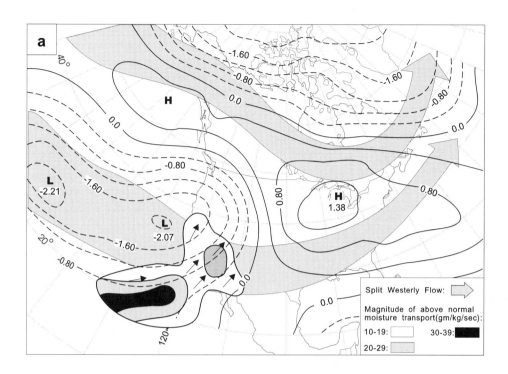

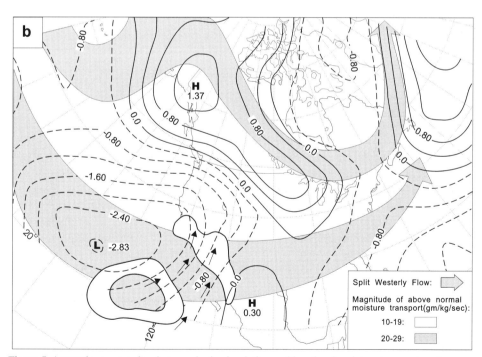

Figure 5. Anomalous upper-level atmospheric circulation and low-level moisture transport: a, January 1993; b, February, 1993. Circulation contour units are standardized anomalies (moisture information from Bell and Basist, 1994).

nating passages of warm and cold storms. This led to a complex sequence of events whereby snow accumulation and subsequent snowmelt, aided by rain falling on the snow, greatly augmented the amount of runoff.

Snowmelt caused by rain falling on snow was one of the most important hydroclimatic processes affecting the 1993 flooding. The temporal distribution of successive flood peaks during the course of the winter appeared to be a direct result of this phenomenon and its relation to the alternation of warm and cold storms. The relationship between rain-on-snow and runoff is illustrated in Figure 6. The daily variation in snowpack depth from December through February is shown, plotted with daily precipitation totals (rain and snow) for the Pinetop Fish Hatchery climate station in the Salt River Basin and the Flagstaff 4 SW climate station in the Verde River Basin (see Fig. 1 for approximate locations). These stations are representative of conditions throughout the high-elevation areas of the state where flooding was generated, particularly in the Salt and Verde River Basins.

The relationship between snow depth and precipitation at each station indicates the importance of both the occurrence and the timing of rain on snow in generating the largest floods. The antecedent conditions for flooding were initiated in early December when a cold front passage associated with a deep trough and upper-level cutoff low delivered large amounts of precipitation (rain at low elevations, snow at high) and a deep snowpack accumulated. Snow depths remained fairly constant throughout most of the month, with some minor variations in snowpack thickness occurring in response to winter cold front passages and intervening warming, respectively. However, during the last week of December 1992, a warm, subtropical storm moved into the state and dropped large quantities of rainfall. This subtropical event raised the snow level above about 2,590 m (8,500 ft; National Oceanic and Atmospheric Administration, 1992). Although depletion of the snowpack began during warming prior to the storm, the rain falling on the snow accelerated the depletion. However, as is evident in Figure 6, much of the snowmelt followed the rain event rather than coincided with it, especially at Flagstaff. Stream discharges rose in response to this event, but major flooding did not occur, probably because significant amounts of rain did not continue to fall during or after the period of most rapid snowmelt. Nonetheless, the December precipitation and snowmelt thoroughly saturated the soil in drainage basins at all elevations throughout much of Arizona. This had important consequences for establishing the antecedent conditions that intensified subsequent flooding (Fig. 6).

The four major storms

The floods in Arizona were caused by at least 16 storms that passed over Arizona from December 1992 through February 1993 (House, 1993; NOAA, 1992, 1993a, 1993b). Most of the storms contributed to runoff and were important for developing and maintaining the antecedent conditions of soil saturation and accumulated snowpack necessary for the floods. However, four of the storms were the principal catalysts for the largest pulses of flooding that occurred during January and February. The

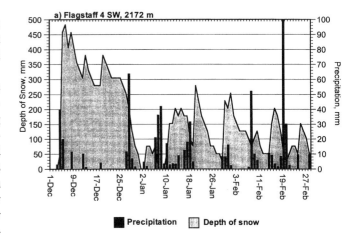

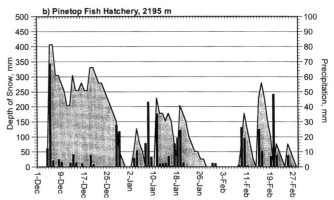

Figure 6. The relationship between precipitation and snow depth for two high-elevation stations in Arizona, December 1992 through February 1993: a, Flagstaff 4 SW; b, Pinetop Fish Hatchery. Precipitation shown corresponds to rain and snow. Data from National Oceanic and Atmospheric Administration (1992, 1993a, and 1993b).

number of individual storms that entered the region and the relative position of each storm track in relation to the position and characteristics of previous storms were reflected in the distribution of flood peaks throughout the state during this time period. Many streams had record or near record peaks in early January; others had record peaks in early February or late February. Some basins in the central portion of Arizona had large floods in response to each of the four major storm episodes that occurred. This rather complicated scenario is illustrated in Figure 7 with a series of normalized hydrographs for selected, unregulated basins in Arizona. Streams in the Central Highlands region best exhibited the four-peak flooding response.

The four major storms are defined for purposes of analysis as follows: (1) January 6–9, (2) January 13–19, (3) February 7–10, and (4) February 18–21. These time periods were chosen to best isolate the precipitation most directly associated with the major flooding episodes. We have, however, omitted some storms that were locally significant and regionally important in the development of antecedent conditions. Isohyetal maps for the four storm episodes are given in Figure 8, and composite 500-mb upper-air circulation maps for periods roughly coinciding with these four storm periods are shown in Figure 9. The upper-air circulation maps show that a split westerly flow played a role during each of the four storm episodes. During the two main January storms (Figs. 8a-b, 9a-b), a persistent upper-air high pressure ridge in the Gulf of Alaska region was coupled with an equally persistent upper-air low pressure trough immediately to the south. This configuration displaced the southern branch of the North Pacific storm track to lower-than-normal latitudes so that storms and above-normal moisture were transported directly across Arizona (Fig. 5a). The two February storms (Figs. 8c-d, 9c-d) were also guided by an upper-air ridge-and-trough pattern. During these episodes, the Gulf of Alaska pressure ridge took the form of an omega-shaped blocking high pattern, and the attendant low pressure trough intruded deeply into subtropical latitudes, conveying warm, moisture-laden air into the southwestern United States from a more southerly trajectory. This was followed by the passage of a cold front as the trough moved through.

January 6–9. Following the precipitation that fell in December (particularly in the last week), the first major storm in January was the most widespread of the four flood-producing storm events (Fig. 8a). It followed a brief period during which temperatures dropped, precipitation fell, the freezing level dropped to 1,525 m (5,000 ft), and more snow accumulated at high elevations. On January 6, however, the snow level retreated to higher than 2,900 m (9,500 ft) when precipitation began to fall during the passage of a warm front. The warm front was associated with a disturbance of predominantly subtropical origin that was steered into Arizona by the southern branch of the split westerly flow. This system continued to deliver large quantities of rain for three days, with maximum amounts recorded on January 7. The timing of snowmelt and precipitation was optimal for flooding. This storm event virtually eliminated the snowpack in high-elevation parts of most drainage basins because of rain falling on the snow and relatively mild temperatures associated with the storm. More important, considerable rain continued to fall after the snowpack melted. This combination of events, coupled with the melt event at the end of December, culminated in the most regionally significant period of

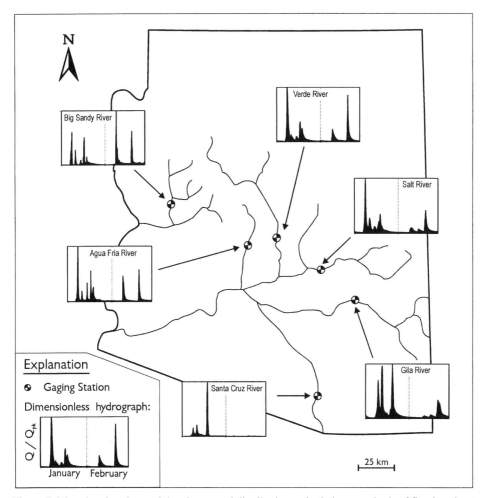

Figure 7. Map showing the spatial and temporal distribution and relative magnitude of flood peaks at selected (unregulated) basins in Arizona, January through February 1993. The vertical axis shows the ratio of hourly discharge to the maximum discharge in the two-month period. Based on data in Smith et al., (1994) and provisional data from the U.S. Geological Survey.

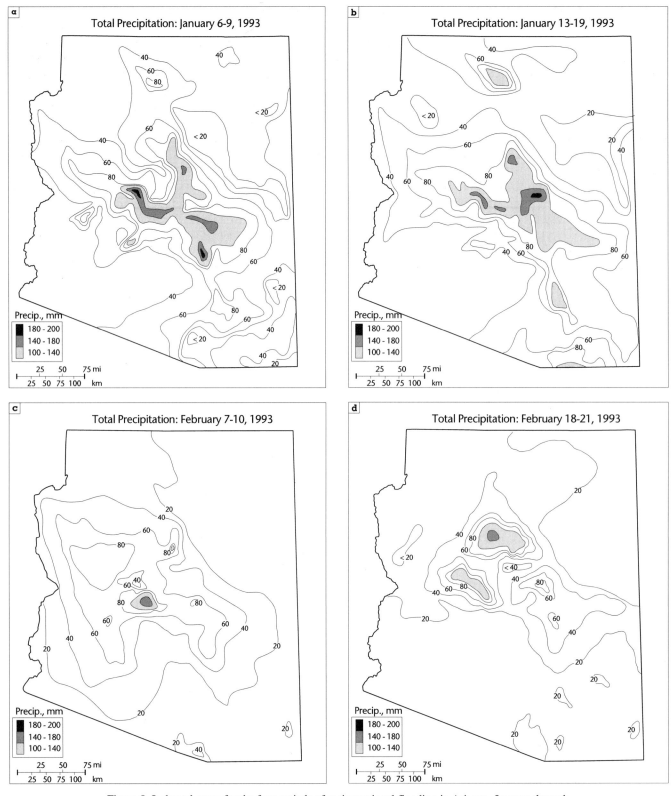

Figure 8. Isohyetal maps for the four periods of major regional flooding in Arizona, January through February 1993. a, January 6–9; b, January 13–19; c, February 7–10; d, February 18–21. Isohyets based on data from National Oceanic and Atmospheric Administration (1993a, 1993b) and unpublished data provided by the Maricopa County Flood Control District and the Salt River Project. Depths in mm. Depths in excess of 100 mm are indicated by shading.

flooding in the entire two-month episode and arguably the largest such episode since at least 1891. Most of the record peaks established in Arizona resulted from this storm (Table 1). Rainfall was particularly intense in the Central Highlands and in the higher ranges of the southeastern Basin and Range (Fig. 8a). Very large basins draining the Central Highlands (Salt and Verde Basins) had exceptionally large floods. Interestingly, flooding on the Santa Cruz River in the southeast was not as severe although several of its tributaries had record or near-record floods (Table 1; Fig. 7; Smith et al., 1994).

January 13–19. The widespread and heavy precipitation of the January 6–9 storm was followed by a similar, but less extreme, flood-producing event in the third week of January. This event culminated in flooding on January 19. During the January 13–19 period several fronts passed through Arizona steered along by the southern branch of the split westerly flow. The rainfall associated with these storms was heavy in the southernmost part of Arizona as well as in portions of the Central Highlands (Fig. 8b). Major flooding occurred along the Santa Cruz River during this episode, and the Gila River received a second pulse of peak flow only days after the first flood crest had attenuated (Fig. 7). At Flagstaff, the relationship between precipitation and snowmelt was less optimal for flooding than that of the early January event (Fig. 6). The snowpack was not depleted, and, in fact, it began to increase near the end of the storm period. Rainfall did not occur during the subsequent snowmelt. At Pinetop, conditions were slightly more favorable for flooding because more snow melt occurred during the initial rainfall. However, by the end of the episode, snow was accumulating there as well.

February 7–10. A shift in the configuration of the large-scale atmospheric circulation preceded the first major storm episode in February. The high-pressure ridge in the Gulf of Alaska shifted slightly to the east and increased in amplitude, bringing the axis of the ridge over western Canada (Fig. 9c). This change was associated with a southward movement of the eastern North Pacific trough and an increase in north-or-south directed flow (meridionality) in the circulation. The result was the continued conveyance of subtropical flow and moisture into the southwest (Fig. 5b) that was directed northward into Arizona behind a warm front. This was rapidly followed by a cold front moving in from the west as the trough passed through. This synoptic situation was especially effective in delivering large amounts of precipitation to western, northwestern, and central parts of Arizona (Fig. 8c). Rivers in these areas, such as the Big Sandy and Agua Fria Rivers, experienced a third large flood during this episode. The Big Sandy River and two of its gauged tributaries recorded peaks of record (Fig. 7; Table 1). This flooding was probably a result of relatively localized, moderate to heavy precipitation on saturated ground with some augmentation by snowmelt. During the cold-front passage that marked the end of this event, some precipitation was delivered in the form of snow, as seen at Flagstaff and Pinetop where snow levels decreased to 2,135 m (7,000 ft) and snowpack depths increased (Fig. 6).

February 18–21. As late February approached, the blocking high-pressure anomaly returned to its earlier position over the Gulf of Alaska, maintaining a split flow in the westerlies and a trough displaced to lower latitudes of the eastern North Pacific (Fig. 9d). Warming occurred in Arizona as a result of the southwesterly flow under this configuration. On February 17, relatively rapid melting of the accumulated snowpack occurred as a result of a regional increase in average daily temperature (near 10 °C [50 °F] at Flagstaff). Beginning late on February 18, this melting episode was dramatically punctuated by precipitation from the last major storm of the season (Fig. 8d). The rapid passage of two fronts in a two-day period produced heavy precipitation over localized areas in the Central Highlands and, in particular, over the central Mogollon Rim in the general vicinity of Flagstaff. This area received extremely high daily totals of precipitation on February 19 and 20. The heavy rain fell on the melting snowpack and resulted in the rapid generation of immense quantities of runoff. Large floods occurred on several streams draining these localized areas (Figs. 10 and 11; Tables 1 and 2). The runoff was concentrated in a small part of the Verde River basin, but it was sufficient to generate the flood of record at the Verde River gauging stations at Paulden, Clarkdale, and Camp Verde (Table 1; Fig. 1). It also amounted to the second-largest flood ever recorded at the gauge below Tangle Creek. A flood of this magnitude coming from such a small part of the basin is evidence of the optimum, flood-enhancing antecedent conditions that existed at the time, and thus, the importance of preceding events in December, January, and most of February.

Rain falling on snow was a very important factor in the generation of the largest 1993 floods, especially in the large basins of the Central Highlands. The strong correspondence between streamflow, snowmelt, and precipitation in the winter of 1992–1993 is shown in Figure 10, where daily values of snowmelt and precipitation at Flagstaff are plotted with the average daily discharge of Oak Creek near Cornville, Arizona. This figure illustrates the sensitivity of stream flow to the timing and relative magnitude of the rainfall in relation to the snowmelt. It suggests that the largest flood peaks will occur when rain falls on snow, accelerating the melting process, and then continues to fall.

THE 1993 FLOODS IN THE VERDE RIVER BASIN

The remaining discussion of the 1993 winter flooding episode in Arizona will focus on flooding in the Verde River Basin during January and February. The Verde River Basin provides an excellent and detailed perspective on many of the important characteristics of the flood episode. Extreme, record-breaking discharges were recorded at all gauges along the Verde River and on most of its principal tributaries during January and February 1993 (Fig. 11). Because of the size, spatial distribution, and diverse physiography of the Verde River Basin, flooding in different portions of the basin exhibited important aspects of the spatial and temporal variation that characterized the flooding throughout Arizona. Additionally, post-1993 flood studies and past research on the paleoflood history of the Verde River allow us to make generalizations about the relative magnitude of the 1993 floods with respect to the largest floods known to have occurred over the last 1,000+ yr (House, 1996; House et al., 1995).

Gauging records from the Verde River Basin

The Verde River Basin spans nearly 15,000 km² (5,800 mi²) of central Arizona. Its headwaters and the headwaters of many of its tributaries encompass a large portion of the Colorado Plateau, but the Central Highlands constitute the bulk of the flood-producing portion of the basin. Four continuous recording gauges are located along the Verde River (Fig. 11). The uppermost gauge is near Paulden, Arizona (USGS gauge no. 09503700). Its contributing drainage area is 5,569 km² (2,150 mi²), which is about 40% of the total basin area. It records runoff draining the Colorado

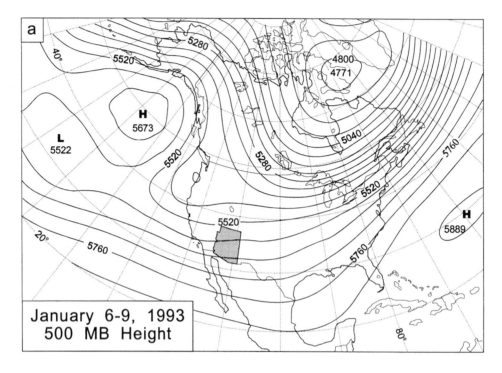

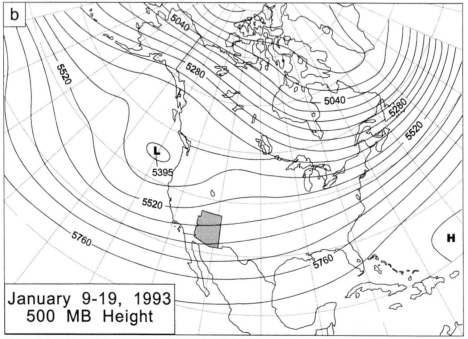

Figure 9 (on this and facing page). Composite 500-mb pressure heights for the four 1993 flood-producing storm episodes. Units are geopotential height in meters above sea level. a, January 6–9; b, January 9–19; c, February 8–10; d, February 19–20.

Plateau and a northeast-facing part of the Central Highlands region. Despite the size of this portion of the Verde Basin, little contribution from it is recorded in the peak discharges at gauges downstream because flood peaks at Paulden usually follow, rather than precede, those at the next gauge downstream by several hours. This lag is probably a result of the relatively elongated shape of the upper basin, circuitous drainage routes, and minor storage effects of Sullivan Lake, just upstream of the gauge (Chin et al., 1991).

Downstream from Paulden, the next gauge is near Clarkdale, Arizona (USGS gauge no. 09504000). Its contributing drainage area is 8,130 km^2 (3,146 mi^2) which accounts for about 60% of the total basin area or 30% of effective flood peak-producing area (i.e., the area below the gauge at Paulden). About 75% of the area between Paulden and Clarkdale is drained by Sycamore and Hell Canyons. Sycamore Canyon is one of the largest single tributaries in the Verde River system. It enters the Verde River from the north, approximately 2.6 km (1 mi) above the gauge. During the 1993 events, Sycamore and Hell Canyons probably accounted for much more than 50% of the runoff at the Clarkdale gauge. Unfortunately, neither one of these tributaries is gauged.

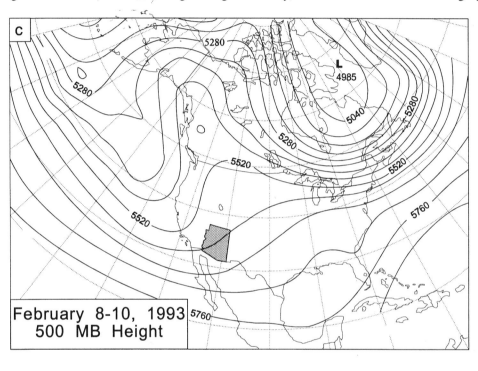

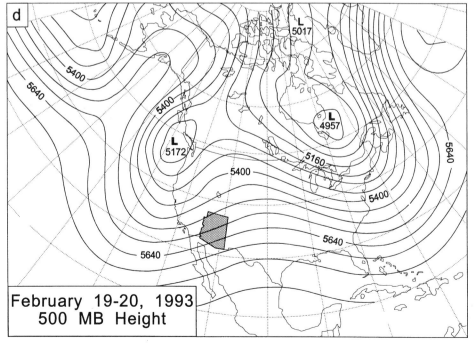

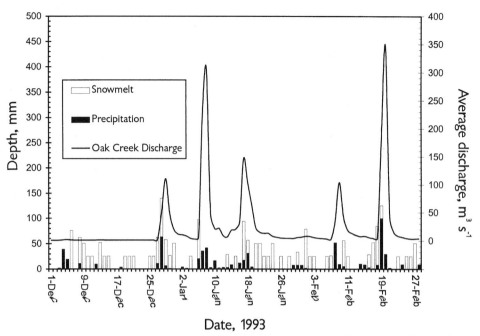

Figure 10. Snowmelt and precipitation at Flagstaff, Arizona, compared with average daily discharge of Oak Creek near Cornville, Arizona (USGS gauge no. 09504400). As shown, snowmelt is the change in the depth of the snowpack and not the actual water content of the melt. Data from National Oceanic and Atmospheric Administration (1992, 1993a, 1993b), Smith et al., (1994), and provisional data from the U.S. Geological Survey.

The gauge below Clarkdale is near Camp Verde, Arizona (USGS gauge no. 09506000). Its contributing drainage area is 12,028 km^2 (4,652 mi^2), which is 85% of total basin area or 75% of the effective area. Between Clarkdale and Camp Verde, four relatively large, gauged tributaries enter the Verde River: Oak Creek (920 km^2, 355 mi^2; USGS gauge no. 09504500), Dry Beaver Creek (368 km^2, 142 mi^2; USGS gauge no. 09505350), Wet Beaver Creek (288 km^2, 111 mi^2; USGS gauge no. 09505200), and West Clear Creek (624 km^2, 241 mi^2; USGS gauge no. 09505800) These gauge sites are shown on Figure 11. The four tributaries account for about 55% of the drainage area between the mainstem gauges of Clarkdale and Camp Verde. Each tributary drains high-elevation terrain on the Colorado Plateau above the southwest face of the Mogollon Rim. Other small, ungauged tributaries from the northeastern side of the Central Highlands also enter the river between the gauges, but their relative contribution is small in relation to the Rim tributaries. The final gauge on the unregulated portion of the Verde River is located below Tangle Creek (USGS gauge no. 09508500). It records runoff from a total of 15,170 km^2 (5,857 mi^2), including an additional 2,200 km^2 (850 mi^2) below the Camp Verde gauge. The majority of this area is within the rugged interior of the Central Highlands. The difference in the hydrographs between Camp Verde and Tangle Creek primarily represents differences in the relative amounts of runoff contributed by the Mogollon Rim and interior Central Highland portions of the basin. Two gauged tributaries enter in this reach: the East Verde River (857 km^2; 331 mi^2; USGS gauge no. 09507980) and Wet Bottom Creek (94 km^2; 36.4 mi^2; USGS gauge no. 09508300).

Many ungauged tributaries also enter in this part of the basin, and they can account for large contributions of runoff.

Flood hydrographs in the Verde River Basin: January and February 1993

The map of the Verde River Basin in Figure 11 shows normalized hydrographs for each gauging station within the basin. The hydrographs exhibit variable responses to the two-month series of storms, and the basinwide pattern is very similar to the statewide pattern depicted in Figure 7. Each of the basins was affected by each flood-producing storm to some degree, and some basins responded to almost every precipitation event in the two-month period. The most pronounced characteristic of the basinwide response was the relative difference between the early January and late February peak discharges within different parts of the basin. The normalized hydrographs indicate that most of the gauges, with the exception of the Verde River at Paulden and Clarkdale, recorded relatively large floods in early January; however, for most sites in the middle and upper parts, the peak in late February was the largest. The early January and late February peak discharges at the Tangle Creek gauge constituted the largest and second-largest peaks recorded at this site, respectively. Their extreme magnitudes were reflected in a massive accumulation of flood debris in a broad alcove less than 1 km (~0.5 mi) above the gauge (Fig. 12). A comparison of the flood hydrographs at different gauges along the main stem of the Verde River (Fig. 13) suggests that different source areas contributed to the peak discharge recorded at the Tangle Creek

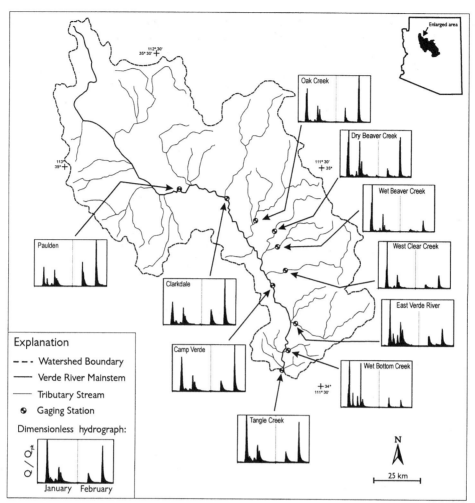

Figure 11. Spatial and temporal distribution and relative magnitude of flood peaks at all gauging stations in the Verde River Basin, January through February 1993. Vertical axis shows the ratio of the hourly discharge to the maximum discharge recorded in the two-month period. Based on data in Smith et al., (1994) and provisional data from the U.S. Geological Survey.

gauge during both major floods. Examination of hydrograph and precipitation data indicates that the relatively small area between Camp Verde and Tangle Creek may have contributed more than 65% of the early January peak. In contrast, during the late February flood, a small part of the basin between Paulden and Camp Verde contributed more than 95% of the peak recorded at Tangle Creek (House, 1996; House et al., 1995).

The early January event. The early January event is the largest recorded discharge at the gauge below Tangle Creek and the third-largest discharge recorded at the gauge near Camp Verde. The discharges were 4,106 m^3 s^{-1} (145,000 ft^3 s^{-1}) and 2,478 m^3 s^{-1} (87,500 ft^3 s^{-1}), respectively. At the Tangle Creek site, the only officially recognized flood larger than 1993 was the flood of February 1891, which is reported as 4,248 m^3 s^{-1} (150,000 ft^3 s^{-1}; Patterson and Somers, 1966).

The occurrence of peak discharge at the Paulden, Clarkdale, and Camp Verde gauges followed the peak at the downstream

Tangle Creek gauge by varying amounts. Because the peak at the Camp Verde gauge followed the peak at the Tangle Creek gauge by four hours, we can assume that only a portion of the rising limb of the Camp Verde hydrograph contributed directly to the peak recorded downstream (Fig. 13a; Table 2). This suggests that an immense amount of runoff from the interior Central Highlands had to have been introduced to the river between the two stations—on the order of 2,690 m^3 s^{-1} (95,000 ft^3 s^{-1}). The occurrence of maximum discharge later in the afternoon at the gauge near Camp Verde and at most of the middle- and upper-basin tributary gauges contributed significantly to the sustained high flow and enormous volume recorded at the Tangle Creek gauge, where the discharge exceeded 3,960 m^3 s^{-1} (140,000 ft^3 s^{-1}) for more than four hours and exceeded 3,400 m^3 s^{-1} (120,000 ft^3 s^{-1}) for more than 10 hours.

The unusual timing of the early January peaks recorded at the Camp Verde and Tangle Creek gauges arose from a chance

TABLE 2. THE MAGNITUDE AND TIMING OF PEAK DISCHARGES IN THE VERDE RIVER BASIN, JANUARY AND FEBRUARY 1993*

Station	Area	Flood of Jan. 8		Flood of Feb. 20	
		Time	Peak Discharge	Time	Peak Discharge
	(km²)		(m³s⁻¹)		(m³s⁻¹)
Verde River near Paulden	5,569	19:30	257	9:45	657
Verde River near Clarkdale	8,130	13:00	745	4:00	1,507
Oak Creek near Comville	919	11:45	524	3:30	736
Dry Beaver Creek near Rimrock	368	9:15	329	5:15	280
Wet Beaver Creek near Rimrock	287	6:30	453	1:30	107
West Clear Creek near Camp Verde	624	8:00	702	1:00	195
Verde River near Camp Verde	12,028	13:00	2,478	11:00	3,370
East Verde River near Childs	857	8:00†	569	2:45	217
Wet Bottom Creek near Childs	94	7:00	209	0:00	34
Verde River below Tangle Creek	14,227	8:30	4,106	16:00	3,512

*Data from Smith et al., 1994.
†Estimated.

Figure 12. Large debris pile on lower Verde River, March 10, 1993. Photograph by P. A. Pearthree, Arizona Geological Survey.

combination of hydrologic events in the middle basin (the area between the Paulden and Camp Verde gauges) and the lower basin (the area between the Camp Verde and Tangle Creek gauges). Tributary hydrographs indicate that two distinct pulses of peak runoff characterized the early January event (Fig. 14). These pulses of runoff corresponded to similar variations in rainfall recorded in the middle and lower portions of the Verde River Basin. The second peak in the flood hydrographs is greater than the first peak in both portions of the basin, but their relative dif-

ference is greater in the lower basin than in the middle basin. From this relation we conclude that the exceptionally large peak recorded at the Tangle Creek gauge at 8:30 A.M., January 8, resulted from the coincidental, nearly optimal combination of the first peak from the middle basin with the second peak from the lower basin. The subsequent peak recorded at Camp Verde of 2,475 m³ s⁻¹ (87,500 ft³ s⁻¹) at 1:00 P.M., January 8, contributed to the sustained high flow recorded at Tangle Creek for most of the day. This situation illustrates the possibility that considerably different flood magnitudes could have occurred at the Camp Verde and Tangle Creek gauges given slight variations in the timing of rainfall and runoff in different portions of the basin.

The late February event. The late February event exceeded the magnitude of the early January flood at most of the gauging stations in the upper and middle portion of the basin. The limited spatial extent of this storm is evident in the distribution of flood peaks and can be inferred from the precipitation distribution in Figure 8d. The sharp precipitation gradient is reflected in the strikingly different relative magnitudes of the floods at Wet and Dry Beaver Creeks: two basins along the Mogollon Rim that are relatively close together (Fig. 11). At the Tangle Creek gauge, the flood of February 19, 1993, was 3,510 m³ s⁻¹ (124,000 ft³ s⁻¹), which is the second-largest peak recorded at this site. At the gauge near Camp Verde, the peak discharge was 3,370 m³ s⁻¹ (119,000 ft³ s⁻¹), which is the largest discharge recorded there. In striking contrast to the early January flood, examination of hydrological and meteorological data suggests that the vast majority of the peak and volume of the late February flood came from only a small part of the basin between Paulden and Camp Verde (Fig. 13b). Most of the runoff in the late February flood came from Oak Creek, Dry Beaver Creek, and probably Sycamore and Hell Canyons. The runoff was relatively flashy as compared with the early January event, and the corresponding total flow volume was considerably less at each gauge site (e.g., less than about 50% of the total volume of the January flood at Tangle Creek).

Gauge records from late February clearly indicate the importance of runoff contributions from Oak and Dry Beaver Creeks; however, the critical roles of Sycamore and Hell Canyons can only be inferred by comparing the Paulden and Clarkdale hydrographs. Figure 13 and Table 2 show that there is a significant lag in the timing of the peaks at Paulden and Clarkdale, with the Paulden gauge recording a peak after the Clarkdale gauge in both the January and February events. This indicates that little of the runoff at the Paulden gauge was a source for the peak discharge at Clarkdale in either event. In the largest flood in late February, the discharge increased from less than about 113 to 1,510 m³ s⁻¹ (4,000 to 53,200 ft³ s⁻¹) between the gauges at Paulden and Clarkdale. It is likely that much of this runoff came from Sycamore and Hell Canyons, which make up almost 75% of the area between the gauges. Meteorological data from Flagstaff and Williams, Arizona, near the upper watershed of Sycamore Canyon, show that the rainfall and flooding conditions in the basin may have been equal to or

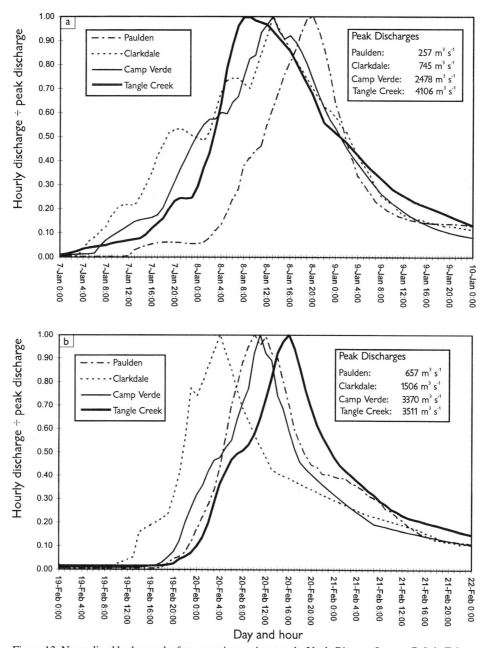

Figure 13. Normalized hydrographs from gauging stations on the Verde River, a, January 7–9; b, February 19–21. Based on data in Smith et al., (1994) and provisional data from the U.S. Geological Survey.

more extreme than those in the watershed of Oak Creek (which is 25% smaller than Sycamore Canyon).

    These differences in the timing of flood peaks indicate that in both the early January and late February events, less than 50%, and perhaps as little as 25%, of the basin contributed to the peak discharges recorded at the Tangle Creek gauge. In the case of the January event, runoff delivered from the entire basin eventually contributed to an immense volume of runoff, but in the late February case, the delivery of runoff was much more limited in space and time, so the flow duration and total volume were considerably lower at the Tangle Creek gauge. It is clear

from the basis of these two events that a larger flood could be generated under more optimal flood-enhancing circumstances in the Verde River Basin. Paleoflood hydrology provides a framework from which to address the possibility for larger floods by directly examining evidence for them in the geological record.

PALEOHYDROLOGICAL CONTEXT OF THE 1993 FLOODS

    Paleoflood hydrology is a geological approach to the study of the magnitude and frequency of large floods that occurred prior to, or in absence of, systematic observation (Baker, 1987,

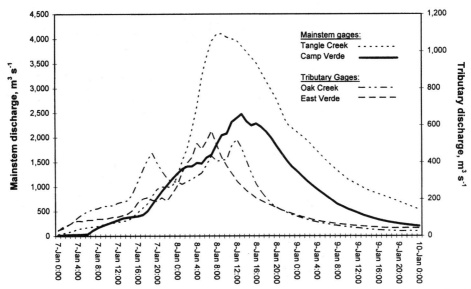

Figure 14. Comparison of mainstem Verde River flood hydrographs with tributary stream flood hydrographs, January 7–10, 1993. Based on data in Smith et al., (1994) and provisional data from the U.S. Geological Survey.

1989; Costa, 1987a). Extensive paleoflood research has been carried out in Arizona, and much of the paleoflood data from rivers throughout the state has been combined to establish a regional paleoflood chronology that spans 5,000 yr (Ely, 1992; Ely et al., 1993). This wealth of paleohydrological data provides a unique opportunity to evaluate the 1993 events in the context of the Holocene history of flooding in central Arizona.

Much of the Arizona paleoflood data has been obtained using the slackwater deposit–paleostage indicator (SWD-PSI) method (Baker, 1987, 1989). This approach involves relating geological evidence for extreme flooding in bedrock canyons to discharge-dependent water surface profiles calculated from a fixed boundary hydraulic model (O'Connor and Webb, 1988). The primary types of geologic evidence for flooding are flood slackwater deposits (SWD), which consist of sand and silt that accumulate in areas of markedly reduced flow velocities during large floods. In many bedrock canyons, deposits from the largest floods are often found in areas protected from low and moderate flow events, where they can persist for hundreds to thousands of years, particularly in arid and semiarid climates (Kochel and Baker, 1988). Age estimates can be obtained for individual deposits using radiocarbon dating techniques on organic material within or between them or with age constraints based on the presence of diagnostic archaeological artifacts. The presence of multiple deposits in a stratigraphic sequence allows for a relative age relationship between deposits to be determined. Paleoflood stages inferred from SWDs can be reinforced or augmented with other types of paleostage indicators (PSIs) including relict high-water marks such as flotsam lines, flood-scoured hill slopes, and flood-damaged vegetation.

SWD-PSI paleoflood studies are suited only to bedrock canyons because stable boundary conditions are assumed in the

modeling, and only in such environments can flood deposits persist for long periods of time and retain their original relationship to the stream channel. On the Verde River, the relation between SWDs from the 1993 floods and the stratigraphy of older flood SWDs has been investigated in such a canyon setting.

Paleohydrological context of the 1993 floods in the Verde Basin

SWD-PSI paleoflood studies on two reaches of the Verde River between the Camp Verde and Tangle Creek gauge sites have produced a detailed, well-constrained paleoflood chronology that spans more than 1,000 yr (Ely and Baker, 1985; O'Connor et al., 1986). Post-1993 flood investigations of the SWD stratigraphy at selected sites in these reaches have provided valuable information regarding the relative magnitude of the 1993 event in the context of this long record of flooding (House, 1996; House et al., 1995). The stratigraphic column shown in Figure 15 is a schematic depiction of a trench in a sequence of flood deposits examined in June 1993. The trench is in an isolated alcove well protected from low- and moderate-magnitude floods along the river. This new site supplements a previous paleoflood study of this reach by O'Connor et al. (1986). Our interpretation of the stratigraphy incorporates evidence specific to this site combined with inferences derived from well-described flood stratigraphy from the paleoflood site downstream (Ely and Baker, 1985). Age designations shown in the figure are taken from those determined for deposits at the downstream reach that we infer to be correlative. Our inference is supported by examination of the downstream sites following the floods and the observation of similar relationships between individual flood deposits and their associated flood magnitude estimates.

The discharges reported in Figure 15 are from a rating curve for this site that was derived from step-backwater modeling of a 500-m (1,640-ft) reach of the river (House, 1996; House et al., 1995). The 1993 peak discharge through the reach is well constrained by records from the Camp Verde gauge (upstream) and the Tangle Creek gauge (downstream). The paleoflood discharges are based on the corresponding SWD elevations and have been adjusted upward to reflect the difference between the heights of diagnostic peak stage indicators (flotsam) and SWDs from the largest 1993 flood at this site (House et al., 1995).

The uppermost deposit in the section is probably correlative to the uppermost deposit at the downstream site based on stratigraphic relations and comparable discharge estimates. At the downstream site, the maximum age of the deposit has been esti-

mated to be approximately 1000 B.P. based on diagnostic archaeological artifacts found on the surface and a radiometric date of in situ charcoal (Ely and Baker, 1985). The underlying unit (unit 2) predates unit 1 by an unknown amount. Unit 2 is separated from unit 4 by a layer of hillslope colluvium, which suggests a relatively long hiatus in flood deposition; the lack of any absolute age control, however, precludes any age designation more specific than that it is older than unit 1. Unit 3 is interpreted as a deposit inset into the colluvial unit separating units 2 and 4. Based on similarities in stratigraphic relationships and discharge estimates from the downstream site, this unit is inferred to be from the 1891 flood. However, this correlation is tenuous. Unit 5 is the deposit from the largest of the 1993 floods at this site. Its stratigraphic relationship

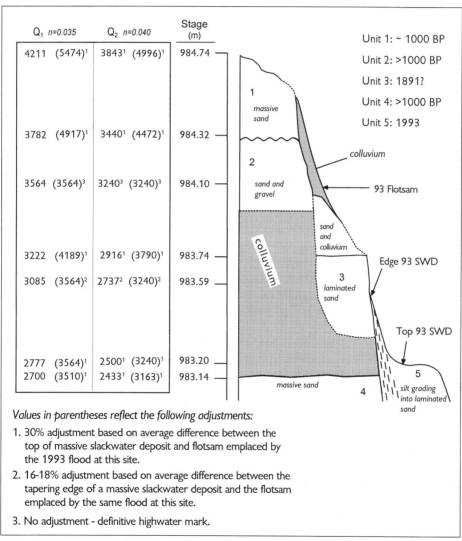

Figure 15. Schematic depiction of flood slackwater deposit (SWD) stratigraphy at the paleoflood site discussed in the text. Discharges shown at left (Q_1 and Q_2) are from step-backwater modeling of a 500-m (1,640-ft) reach of the river using two different estimates of channel roughness (n). Discharges reflect correction for differences in flood stage inferred from different types of highwater marks (flotsam versus slackwater deposits) from the largest 1993 flood at this site. Several tributaries that enter the river between this site and the gauge below Tangle Creek experienced significant flooding in the winter of 1993 (see House et al., 1995, for detailed discussion).

to the rest of the sequence is obvious. We note that the dramatic increase in discharge of the early January flood between Camp Verde and Tangle Creek was such that the peak discharge was less than that of the late February flood at this site (House, 1996; House et al., 1995). However, as a result of the dramatic increase in flood discharge described previously, the early January flood was the largest at sites farther downstream.

In the flood stratigraphy at this site there is evidence for at least five large floods. Three are larger than the 1993 flood; of these, two occurred prior to 1000 B.P., and one occurred slightly more than a century ago (probably in 1891). The two oldest floods were considerably larger than the 1993 event, whereas the 1993 event and the inferred 1891 event were similar in magnitude. The magnitude of the 1891 flood in the vicinity of the Tangle Creek gauge is estimated to be only slightly larger than the 1993 flood, which is consistent with our stratigraphic interpretation and that of Ely and Baker (1985). There is also evidence at this site for a flood that was slightly smaller than the 1993 flood, which must have occurred prior to 1000 B.P. (unit 4).

Regional peak flood magnitude characteristics

Combining the regional paleoflood data with all gauged and historical flood discharge data from Arizona (including the record-breaking 1993 peaks) illustrates an interesting relationship in regional flood magnitude–drainage area relationships. The plot shown in Figure 16 depicts the largest gauged, historical, and paleoflood discharges for drainage basins of varying area in the Lower Colorado River Basin (see Enzel et al., 1993). An envelope curve delimits the maximum values of the data spread. The position of the curve is based only on gauged and historical flood data (including U.S. Geological Survey indirect estimates from miscellaneous sites). The addition of the paleoflood values to the plot effectively extends the temporal base of the data set in real time, in some cases by hundreds to thousands of years. Because all of the paleoflood values fall on or very near the curve, it has been proposed as a reasonable approximation of a natural upper bound on flood magnitudes in this region that has persisted for the last several thousand years (Enzel et al., 1993).

Comparing the 1993 record flood peaks to this figure provides an interesting perspective on the relative magnitude of this major winter flooding episode. From this comparison, it is clear that many individual flood peaks in 1993 were quite large, but all were within the realm of documented natural tendencies of extreme floods in the region, as the Verde River paleoflood data attest. Some flood peaks from the larger basins were relatively close to the envelope, whereas record floods in basins less than about 1,000 km² (~400 mi²) were small in relation to the curve, because extreme floods in small basins within the region usually result from localized, intense thunderstorms. The plot also indicates that basins without paleoflood records experienced floods comparable to, and in some cases larger than, the largest paleofloods recorded in basins of similar sizes.

DISCUSSION

The immense regional scale of the 1993 flooding episode is encapsulated in Figure 16. Considering the regional scale and the magnitude of individual events in the largest basins, we contend that the anomalous hydroclimatological conditions that characterized the 1993 floods are probably analogous to those associated with most of the large paleofloods in the largest basins. The sequence of events culminating in the 1993 flood episode illustrates that certain hydroclimatological phenomena are extremely conducive to the generation of huge floods on large rivers in Arizona, particularly in the Central Highlands Province. These phenomena include abnormally high rainfall totals throughout the region, repeated accumulation and melting of heavy snowpack, direct rainfall on snowpack, and prolonged periods of relatively moderate intensity rainfall over large areas and of high intensity rainfall over smaller areas. Each of these processes in 1993 was initiated and perpetuated by a persistent, anomalous circulation pattern that repeatedly steered alternately warm and cold storms into the region along a southerly displaced storm track over a three-month period. The scale of these phenomena was such that streams throughout much of the state experienced severe flooding.

Evidence for larger floods in the paleoflood record thus suggests more extreme variations on the hydroclimatic scenario played out in 1993. Furthermore, optimal basinwide timing of flood runoff coming from a similar set of circumstances might also produce events large enough to have emplaced the paleoflood deposits. Recall that a larger peak on the Verde River might have occurred in January 1993 were it not for relatively slight variations in the timing of precipitation and runoff in different portions of the basin.

In a summary treatment of paleoflood chronologies from the southwestern United States, Ely (1992) and Ely et al., (1993) proposed that there is an indication of temporal clustering of large floods that is consistent with evidence of hydrological variability inferred from other types of proxy indicators of regional climate change over the last 5,000 yr. The periods of apparent clustering defined by Ely et al. (1993) were determined by stratigraphic evidence (SWDs) of approximately synchronous regional flooding. Their analysis suggested that the timing of clusters of large floods corresponds to periods of transitions in the regional climate. The interpretation of the 1993 floods in the context of regional hydroclimatological phenomena stemming from global circulation characteristics offers important insights into the physical basis of flood clustering in the paleorecord in the southwestern United States.

The 1993 flood scenario provides a convincing modern analogue for the processes that probably operated to generate comparably large paleofloods. Hence we suggest that clusters of flooding in the paleorecord of the Southwest are best explained by a global circulation scenario involving an unusually high frequency of winters characterized by a southerly displaced Pacific storm track enhanced by subtropical flow. The key factor in this scenario is the development of a circulation anomaly in the eastern North Pacific Ocean that promotes the formation of a split flow in the westerlies

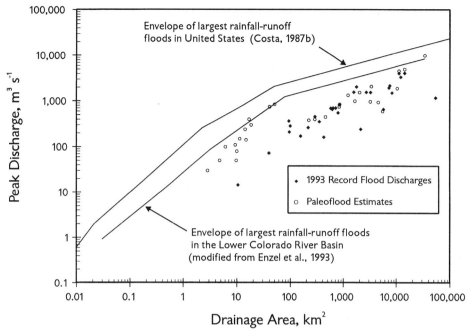

Figure 16. Comparison of the 1993 record flood peaks from unregulated basins to paleofloods and the envelope curve of the maximum gauged and historical floods in the lower Colorado River basin. Envelope curve slightly modified from Enzel et al., (1993). Also shown is the envelope curve for the largest floods in the United States as of 1987 (Costa, 1987b).

and forces the southern branch of the normal Pacific storm track to lower latitudes. Such a winter pattern has been associated with ENSO conditions over the last 100+ yr (e.g., in the winters of 1890–1991, 1964–1965, 1979–1980, 1992–1993, 1993–1994) but might also develop independent of an El Niño in response to other kinds of global circulation changes.

CONCLUDING REMARKS

We have shown that the 1993 Arizona flood sequence was comparable in terms of regional scale and individual flood magnitudes to the largest-known flooding episodes in this region over at least the last 1,000 yr, and possibly as long as the last 5,000 yr. The 1993 episode resulted from a distinctive combination of hydroclimatological and hydrological events. During the middle and late Holocene, such events have characterized periods of climatic transition, both regionally and globally (Ely et al., 1993). Taken in the context of the paleoflood record and its connection to regional hydroclimatological phenomena, characteristics of the 1993 flood episode are remarkably consistent with documented regional trends in the temporal variability of extreme flooding in the southwestern United States.

We have identified the winter season conditions of atmospheric circulation on global, hemispheric, and regional scales that resulted in significant and persistent flooding in Arizona during 1993. ENSO-related ocean-atmosphere interactions supported the development of an atmospheric circulation anomaly in the eastern North Pacific Ocean that included a blocking high-pressure pattern over the Gulf of Alaska. An associated split jet stream deflected the storm track southward across the southwestern United States and directed a long sequence of significant winter storms across Arizona.

We have also established the paleohydrological context of the 1993 floods along the Verde River by comparing their sedimentological evidence with similar evidence from comparably large and even larger floods that have occurred over the past 1,000 yr. We conclude that the anomalous hydroclimatological conditions associated with the 1993 floods are characteristic of the types of conditions that were required to generate the floods of comparable or greater magnitude that are evident in the paleoflood record.

The paleoflood record on the Verde River indicates that, although the 1993 floods were rare and extreme events, they were not unprecedented. This unique information is afforded only by the geological evidence, and it should serve as a clear reminder that such extreme events are inevitable outcomes of natural processes. Similar occurrences in the future are certain. Knowledge of the hydroclimatological and paleohydrological context of the 1993 Arizona flood sequence can serve as a tool for flood hydrologists, water supply managers, and floodplain managers to better understand the physical processes associated with extreme floods and their inherent patterns. An enhanced understanding could lead to better management policies and better water-supply forecasting and reservoir management over both the long and short terms as well as a greater ability to foresee local consequences of regional and global climatic phenomena.

ACKNOWLEDGMENTS

Many people helped in the preparation of this manuscript. We owe particular thanks to Chris Smith of the USGS, Tucson, for allowing free access to the USGS hydrological data base. Steve Waters of the Maricopa County Flood Control District and Dallas Reigle of the Salt River Project provided supplementary precipitation data. Michelle Wood and Fenbiao Ni of the Tree-Ring Laboratory, University of Arizona, compiled the flood hydroclimatology and atmospheric circulation data and prepared several figures. Pete Corrao and Carrie House helped with preparation of many figures. We are grateful to Vince Cronin of the University of Wisconsin, Milwaukee, for his thoughtful and comprehensive review of the manuscript. This research was supported in part by the Salt River Project, Arizona; the Arizona Geological Survey; the Quaternary Sciences Center of the Desert Research Institute; the Hydrological Sciences Program of the National Science Foundation, grant EAR-9305252; the U.S. Geological Survey Water Resources Research Grant Program, award # 14-08-0001-G1754; the Climate and Global Change Program of the National Oceanic and Atmospheric Administration, grant GC94-504; and the National Institute for Global Environmental Change–Western Regional Center, Research Agreement No. W/GEC 92-020. This manuscript is part of the senior author's doctoral dissertation and is contribution #41 from the Arizona Laboratory for Paleohydrological and Hydroclimatological Analysis (ALPHA), Department of Geosciences, University of Arizona.

REFERENCES CITED

Baker, V. R., 1987, Paleoflood hydrology and extraordinary flood events: Journal of Hydrology, v. 96, p. 79–99.

Baker, V. R., 1989, Magnitude and frequency of paeleofloods, *in* Beven, K., and Carling, P., eds., Floods: Hydrological, sedimentological, and geomorphological implications: New York, John Wiley, p. 171–183.

Bell, G. D., and Basist, A. N., 1994, The global climate of December 1992–February 1993. Part I: Warm ENSO conditions continue in the tropical Pacific; California drought abates: Journal of Climate, v. 7, p. 1581–1605.

Chin, E. H., Aldridge, B. N., and Longfield, R. J., 1991, Floods of February 1980 in southern California and central Arizona: U.S. Geological Survey Professional Paper 1494, 126 p.

Costa, J. E., 1987a, A history of paleoflood hydrology in the United States: 1800–1970, *in* Landa, E. R., and Ince, S., eds., The history of hydrology, history of geophysics, v. 3: Washington, D.C., American Geophysical Union, p. 49–53.

Costa, J. E., 1987b, A comparison of the largest rainfall-runoff floods in the United States with those of the People's Republic of China and the world: Journal of Hydrology, v. 96, p. 101–115.

Ely, L. L., 1992, Large floods in the southwestern United States in relation to late Holocene climatic variations [Ph.D. thesis]: Tucson, University of Arizona, 326 p.

Ely, L. L., and Baker, V. R., 1985, Reconstructing paleoflood hydrology with slackwater deposits: Verde River, Arizona: Physical Geography, v. 6, p. 103–126.

Ely, L. L., Enzel, Y., Baker, V. R., and Cayan, D. R., 1993, A 5000-year record of extreme floods and climate change in the southwestern United States: Science, v. 262, p. 410–412.

Ely, L. L., Enzel, Y., and Cayan, D. R., 1994, Anomalous north Pacific atmospheric circulation and large winter floods in the southwestern United States: Journal of Climate, v. 7, p. 977–987.

Enzel, Y., Ely, L. L., House, P. K., Baker, V. R., and Webb, R. H., 1993, Paleoflood evidence for a natural upper bound to flood magnitudes in the Colorado River Basin: Water Resources Research, v. 29, p. 2287–2297.

Guttman, N. B., Lee, J. J., and Wallis, J. R., 1993, Heavy winter precipitation in southwest Arizona: Eos (Transactions, American Geophysical Union), v. 74, p. 482–485.

Hirschboeck, K. K., 1985, Hydroclimatology of flow events in the Gila River Basin, central and southern Arizona [Ph.D. thesis]: Tucson, University of Arizona, 335 p.

Hirschboeck, K. K., 1987, Hydroclimatically-defined mixed distributions in partial duration flood series, *in* Singh, V. P., ed., Hydrologic frequency modeling: Boston, D. Reidel Publishing, p. 199–212.

Hirschboeck, K. K., 1988, Flood hydroclimatology, *in* Baker, V. R., Kochel, R. C., and Patton, P. C., eds., Flood geomorphology: New York, John Wiley & Sons, p. 27–50.

House, P. K., 1993, The Arizona floods of January and February 1993: Arizona Geology, v. 23, p. 1–9.

House, P. K., 1996, Reports on applied paleoflood hydrological investigations in western and central Arizona [Ph.D. thesis]: Tucson, University of Arizona, 356 p.

House, P. K., Pearthree, P. A., and Fuller, J. E., 1995, Hydrologic and paleohydrologic assessment of the 1993 floods in the Verde River, central Arizona: Arizona Geological Survey Open-file Report 95-20, 23 p.

Huckleberry, G. A., 1994, Contrasting channel response to floods on the middle Gila River, Arizona: Geology, v. 22, p. 1083–1086.

Kochel, R. C., and Baker, V. R., 1988, Paleoflood analysis using slackwater deposits, *in* Baker, V. R., Kochel, R. C., and Patton, P. C., eds., Flood geomorphology: New York, John Wiley & Sons, p. 357–376.

MacNish, R. D., Smith, C. F., and Goddard, K. E., 1993, Floods in Arizona, January 1993: U.S. Geological Survey Open-File Report 93-54, 2 p.

National Oceanic and Atmospheric Administration, 1992, Arizona, *in* Climatological data (U.S. Department of Commerce), December 1992, v. 96, n. 12, p. 6–8.

National Oceanic and Atmospheric Administration, 1993a, Arizona, *in* Climatological data (U.S. Department of Commerce), January 1993, v. 97, n. 1, p. 6–8.

National Oceanic and Atmospheric Administration, 1993b, Arizona, *in* Climatological data (U.S. Department of Commerce), February 1993, v. 97, n. 2, p. 6–8.

O'Connor, J. E., and Webb, R. H., 1988, Hydraulic modeling for paleoflood analysis, *in* Baker, V. R., Kochel, R. C., and Patton, P. C., eds., Flood geomorphology: New York, John Wiley & Sons, p. 393–402.

O'Connor, J. E., Fuller, J. E., and Baker, V. R., 1986, Late Holocene flooding within the Salt River Basin, central Arizona: Unpublished report to the Salt River Project, Tempe, Arizona, 60 p.

Patterson, J. L., and Somers, W. P., 1966, Magnitude and frequency of floods in the United States. Part 9: Colorado River Basin: U.S. Geological Survey Water-Supply Paper 1683, 476 p.

Roeske, R., Garrett, J., and Eychaner, J., 1989, Floods of October 1983 in southeastern Arizona: U.S. Geological Survey Water-Resources Investigations Report 85-4225-C, 77 p.

Sellers, W. D., and Hill, R. H., 1974, Arizona climate, 1931–1972: Tucson, University of Arizona Press, 616 p.

Smith, C. F., Rigas, P. D., Ham, L. K., Duet, N. R., and Anning, D. W., 1994, Water resources data, Arizona, Water year 1993: U.S. Geological Survey Water-Data Report AZ-93-1, 360 p.

U.S. Army Corps of Engineers, 1994, Flood damage report, State of Arizona, floods of 1993: U.S. Army Corps of Engineers, Los Angeles District, South Pacific Division, 107 p.

Webb, R. H., and Betancourt, J. L., 1992, Climatic variability and flood frequency of the Santa Cruz River, Pima County, Arizona: U.S. Geological Survey Water-Supply Paper 2379, 40 p.

Manuscript Accepted by the Society January 29, 1997

Geological Society of America
Reviews in Engineering Geology, Volume XI
1997

Gas pipeline erosion failures: January 1993 floods, Gila River Basin, Arizona

Brian J. Doeing and David T. Williams
WEST Consultants, Inc., 2111 Palomar Airport Road, Suite 180, Carlsbad, California 92009
Jeffrey B. Bradley
WEST Consultants, Inc., 2101 4th Avenue, Suite 1050, Seattle, Washington 98121

ABSTRACT

Flooding occurred throughout Arizona in January 1993 as a result of record precipitation, early snow melt, and saturated soil conditions. The high flows in the Gila River and its tributaries caused failure, damage, or exposure of many natural gas pipelines crossing rivers, streams, and washes. This chapter presents a case study of erosion analysis for six El Paso Natural Gas Company (EPNG) pipelines that failed or were exposed in Arizona during January 1993. The failures were critical because these were major transmission pipelines that supplied natural gas to residential and industrial users in whole communities and groups of communities. The scour evaluations conducted were significant because they provided a scientific and engineering basis for emergency pipeline replacement or repair.

Detailed scour and sediment transport studies were conducted to compute the design scour depth for pipeline replacement. The studies incorporated a hydrological analysis for the 100-yr design flood, surveys of channel geometry for hydraulic computations, and geotechnical analyses of sediment samples for grain-size distribution in the streambed. The scour part of the studies considered not only vertical scour but also lateral scour due to bank erosion, channel meander migration, and channel braiding. The scour studies were used in the design, construction, and permitting process to expedite replacement of the pipelines. For many of these pipelines, it was the first time that the engineering methods of river hydraulics and sediment transport and the science of river morphology were used in the pipeline crossing design.

INTRODUCTION

Many of the effects of the 1992–1993 winter storms and record rainfall runoff in southern California and Arizona were plainly visible, such as the flooding of homes, businesses, and croplands as a result of high stages in rivers and streams, the destruction of bridges and roadways, and the loss of land where stream banks eroded or where river channels migrated into new areas. One major effect of flooding not as readily apparent was the scour of the streambeds. In some cases when scour occurs during flooding, little evidence may remain after the water subsides. This is the case when sediment is deposited in the scour hole during the recession limb of the runoff hydrograph (Chang, 1988).

Scour caused the failure of a number of gas transmission pipelines crossing streams in the Gila River Basin in central and southwestern Arizona during the floods of January 1993. Buried pipelines were undermined by vertical scour of the streambed; elevated pipelines on bridges were damaged or at risk from scour at bridge piers and abutments. Pipelines were also damaged at the channel banks and in the floodplain outside the active channel. Many of the pipelines had been buried without the benefit of a detailed river hydraulic analysis. The general practice of El Paso Natural Gas Company (EPNG) was to bury a pipeline 1.5 m (5 ft) below the stream bottom, unless evidence of more severe scour potential was apparent. The U.S. Department of Transportation's pipeline safety regulations require that natural gas pipelines installed in navigable waters have a minimum cover of 122 cm (48 in) in soil and 61 cm (24 in) in consolidated rock

Doeing, B. J., Williams, D. T., and Bradley, J. B., 1997, Gas pipeline erosion failures: January 1993 floods, Gila River Basin, Arizona, *in* Larson, R. A., and Slosson, J. E., eds., Storm-Induced Geologic Hazards: Case Histories from the 1992–1993 Winter in Southern California and Arizona: Boulder, Colorado, Geological Society of America Reviews in Engineering Geology, v. XI.

(U.S. Department of Transportation, 1994). Because of the flooding in January 1993, six of EPNG's pipelines needed emergency replacement or repair. Whole communities or groups of communities depended on the gas supplied by these pipelines for heating, cooking, and industrial use.

Because of the emergency situation, little time was available to determine the recommended design burial depths and lateral limits for pipeline burial. In most cases, the time available was controlled by the time it took to obtain replacement pipe or permits for repair. Even so, EPNG was determined to conduct detailed scour evaluations at each site to ensure that the pipelines would be safe from future floods up to the 100-yr event. In the following sections we present some background on the Gila River Basin, the 1992–1993 storms, the sediment transport modeling and scour evaluations conducted, and specific details for each of the pipeline crossings.

GILA RIVER BASIN

The Gila River Basin, which comprises 150,700 km^2 (58,200 mi^2), extends from the Continental Divide in southwestern New Mexico to the Colorado River at Yuma, Arizona. The basin includes practically the entire southern half of the state of Arizona (Fig. 1). The river is approximately 1,052 km (654 mi) long and flows in a generally westward course across the state. Some of the major tributaries include the Verde, Salt, Agua Fria, Santa Cruz, and San Pedro Rivers (U.S. Army Corps of Engineers, 1954). Although there are pronounced rainy seasons in the winter months and occasional summer thunderstorms, many of the streams and rivers, such as the Santa Cruz River near Tucson, have no flow during most of the year (Ponce et al., 1985). In addition to the climate and a high rate of infiltration of stream flow into the channel beds in some areas, other reasons for dry channel conditions include storage impoundments and irrigation water diversions. Extreme floods in the basin in recent years occurred in 1978, 1980, and 1983 (Smith et al., 1994; National Oceanic and Atmospheric Administration, 1981).

Ten major dams in the basin are designed to capture runoff and store it for year-round use. Horseshoe Dam and Bartlett Dam on the Verde River are part of the Salt River Project, which also includes five dams on the Salt River: Roosevelt Dam, Horse Mesa Dam, Mormon Flat Dam, Stewart Mountain Dam, and Granite Reef Dam. On the Agua Fria River, Waddell Dam is managed by the U.S. Bureau of Reclamation; on the upper Gila River, Coolidge Dam is managed by the U.S. Bureau of Indian Affairs. Downstream on the Gila River is Painted Rock Dam, which forms the largest reservoir in the basin and is operated by the Los Angeles District, U.S. Army Corps of Engineers. Many of these dams saw record peak outflows as a result of the winter storms of 1992–1993.

1992–1993 STORMS

Unusually intense and prolonged rains in January 1993 caused the most widespread and severe flooding in the State of Arizona since the turn of the century. The greatest rainfall occurred in the area to the north and east of Phoenix, but the entire state received precipitation in excess of 300% of normal. The highest flows of record were observed at some stream-flow gauging stations in every major river basin in the state (MacNish, et al., 1993). The storm patterns were caused by the combination of a vigorous subtropical jet stream with a mean position farther north than normal and a persistent area of high pressure centered over the Gulf of Alaska. In the aftermath of the storms, the Gila River Basin saw the largest volume of runoff since record keeping began in 1888 (U.S. Army Corps of Engineers, 1993a).

The first in a series of Pacific storms brought heavy rains and snow to Arizona during the last week of December 1992. During January 1993, a number of additional storms from the Pacific brought more intensive rainfall. The most significant of these storms occurred January 6–8, January 10–11, January 14–15, and January 17–18. Many precipitation stations in Arizona established new record rainfalls for the month of January. Heavy rainfall over such a short period on already saturated ground was the primary factor contributing to record runoff. A strong secondary factor was early snowmelt. The displaced subtropical jet stream pushed subtropical heat and moisture farther north than normal. Areas that normally do not experience snowmelt until spring received rain on the snow pack that had accumulated from early winter storms. The last major storm system associated with this potent upper air pattern moved out of the state on January 19. As seen in Figure 2, precipitation data from the National Weather Service indicate that rainfall in the State of Arizona during January 1993 ranged from 388 to 572% of normal January precipitation.

RECORD RUNOFF

The long duration of the storm system, coupled with the nearly saturated soil conditions and water-laden snowpack over many Arizona watersheds, caused excessive amounts of runoff in early 1993. This is in contrast to the disastrous storms that hit central Arizona in February 1980, which lasted only nine days. In 1980, only small amounts of runoff resulted from snowmelt, as only one station had less snow water content after the storm compared with before the storm (National Oceanic and Atmospheric Administration, 1981). The National Weather Service reported that in 1993 snowpack was 154% of normal in the Salt–Verde River watershed, and runoff from the snowpack was projected to be 342% of normal. Some of the initial flooding on the small streams resulted in flood discharges with a probability of less than 5% occurring in any given year. The accumulated flow in the larger streams produced many flood discharges with a probability of less than 1 to 2% occurring in any given year. Although flood peak discharges were high, a more significant aspect was the high volume of runoff. Figure 3 compares the expected volume of a flood with a 1% chance occurring in any given year (100-yr flood) to the estimated volume of the January 1993 flood, showing most areas in the Gila River Basin exceeding the 100-yr volumes.

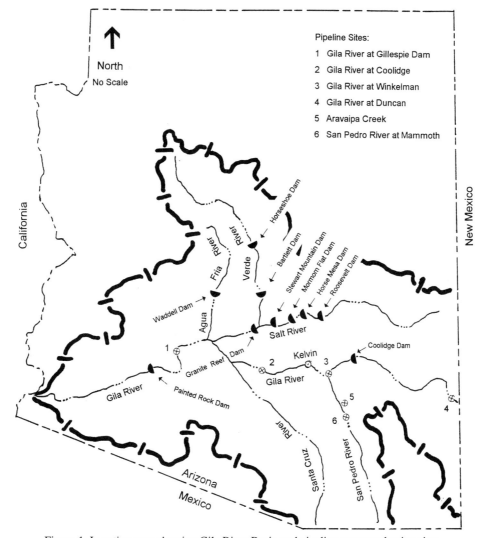

Figure 1. Location map showing Gila River Basin and pipeline scour evaluation sites.

Early in the storm period, reservoirs served to detain flows in the Salt and Gila River systems. Eventually, when available storage was exceeded, reservoir releases were dramatically increased, in some cases several days after the actual storm events. Many of the dams in the basin had record peak discharge outflows in 1993 (Table 1).

Painted Rock Dam, completed in 1958, is located on the Gila River below the other dams and has a storage capacity of 3,100 hm³ (2,500,000 acre ft). The area around the dam is normally arid and the reservoir is usually an empty, dry plain. During the two-month period from January 7 to March 7, 1993, the total inflow volume into the Painted Rock Reservoir was close to 4,900 hm³ (4,000,000 acre ft). The Painted Rock Reservoir became the largest lake in Arizona, spanning 40 km (25 mi) in length and 8 km (5 mi) in width. The estimated return period for a flood with a volume of this magnitude is 500 yr. During this storm period, the maximum inflow into the reservoir had reached 5,100 cubic m per second (180,000 cubic ft per second [cfs]), but the

maximum outflow was only 700 cubic m per second (26,000 cfs). This is the first time in the history of the dam that flow overtopped the emergency spillway (U.S. Army Corps of Engineers, 1993a).

SCOUR EVALUATIONS AND SEDIMENT TRANSPORT MODELING

Approach

The record flood events in the Gila River Basin in January 1993 uncovered a number of EPNG pipelines at steam crossings, causing some of the pipelines to fail. The locations of six of these sites are shown in Figure 1. Under emergency conditions, a scour analysis was performed at each crossing site in order to obtain criteria for pipeline replacement design and construction and to assist in the permitting process. The studies were conducted by hydraulic and sedimentation engineers to evaluate local and general scour and the possible lateral extent

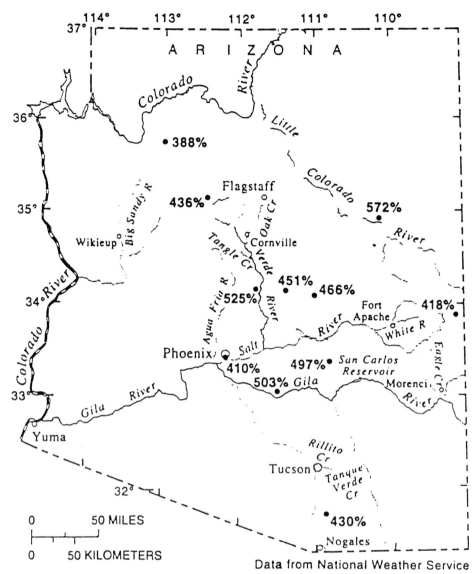

Figure 2. January 1993 precipitation as a percentage of normal January precipitation, after MacNish et al., 1993.

of scour for the 100-yr flood. Recommended pipe burial depths and lateral limits for burial were provided as a result of the studies. Since most rivers in the southwestern United States and in the study area are alluvial, with broad tendencies to meander or braid because of high stream gradients and abundant upstream sediment supply, the scour analysis considered not only vertical scour but also lateral channel migration.

The pipeline failures threatened the continuing natural gas supply to some very large communities. EPNG line numbers 1100 and 1103, which cross the Gila River below Gillespie Dam, supply a large portion of the natural gas used in southern California. Fortunately, alternative loops in the distribution system were tapped to continue deliveries until a temporary line was constructed over the old U.S. Highway 80 bridge. Due to the emergency situation, scour evaluation results were needed as

quickly as possible at each site. Very little time could be allocated for data gathering and refinement of technique. In most cases, preliminary results were required within six weeks to meet pipeline crossing design and material ordering schedules.

To provide the pipeline crossing design information needed by EPNG, scour evaluations were performed with numerical modeling, using field data as input. The procedures are outlined in the flow chart in Figure 4. The process included an initial data search to gather information on stream gauge data; previous hydrologic and hydraulic studies, such as flood insurance studies; prior geotechnical investigations, such as soil borings taken for bridge crossings near the site; and topographic maps and aerial photographs. A field reconnaissance was conducted by hydraulic and sedimentation engineers to obtain hydraulic parameters, such as Manning's "n" values, and to observe channel characteristics

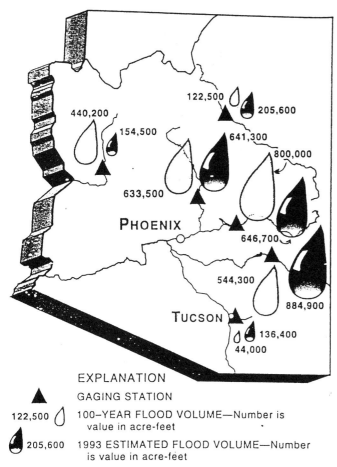

EXPLANATION

▲ GAGING STATION

122,500 ⬭ 100-YEAR FLOOD VOLUME—Number is
value in acre-feet

◖ 205,600 1993 ESTIMATED FLOOD VOLUME—Number
is value in acre-feet

Figure 3. Comparison of flood volume from 100-yr and 1993 floods, after MacNish et al., 1993.

TABLE 1. PEAK SPILLWAY DISCHARGES AT SELECTED DAMS IN 1993

Dam and River	Date	Discharge (m³/s)
Roosevelt Dam, Salt River	19-Jan-1993	1,020
Horse Mesa Dam, Salt River	19-Jan-1993	900
Horseshoe Dam, Verde River	8-Jan-1993	3,140
Bartlett Dam, Verde River	8-Jan-1993	3,110
Granite Reef Diversion Dam, Salt River	9-Jan-1993	3,020
Coolidge Dam, Gila River	20-Jan-1993	930
Painted Rock Dam, Gila River	Mar-1993	740

and the user's manual for the Corps of Engineers Hydrologic Engineering Center. A number of different sediment transport programs exist, but the technique is still in the developing stages. One interagency comparison study of model applicability is still in progress (Fan, 1988). The best chance for successful approximation of a solution to a sediment transport problem with a computer model is achieved when one knows best the assumptions, capabilities, and limitations of the model being applied.

HEC-6 model development

Hydrology. Research was conducted to determine the 100-yr flood and to develop a design flood hydrograph at each crossing. Public and private agencies were contacted for hydrologic information pertinent to the study. Resource agencies included cities and counties, the U.S. Army Corps of Engineers, the Federal Emergency Management Agency (FEMA), the U.S. Geological Survey, the U.S. Bureau of Reclamation, and the Salt River Project. Long-term stream-flow records were used, if necessary, to determine the 100-yr design flood discharge by performing a flood frequency analysis on the historical records (Thomas et al., 1994; U.S. Water Resources Council, 1981; U.S. Army Corps of Engineers, 1992). In most cases, the characteristic shape of the design flood hydrograph was patterned after the highest measured peak flow hydrograph that could be obtained from stream gauges near the pipeline crossing site. This was accomplished by increasing all of the ordinates of the historical hydrograph by the ratio of the design flood peak to the measured flow peak. Figure 5 shows an example of a 100-yr discharge design flood hydrograph. This hydrograph for the Gila River at Coolidge was patterned after the January 9, 1993, measured hydrograph at Kelvin.

Channel geometry. An HEC-2 model was developed for each stream crossing in order to develop the hydraulic basis for the sediment transport analysis. Field surveys were taken to determine the geometry of the channel within the study reach. In general, five to 10 cross sections were obtained upstream of the pipeline crossing and three to five were obtained downstream. These locations suit the determination of backwater hydraulics at the pipeline crossing site and the movement of sediment from the upstream direction. If a recent HEC-2 model was available, it was supplemented with the surveyed cross sections of the river

and river morphology. Locations were determined for bed material sampling and for surveys of channel cross-section geometry.

A hydrologic analysis was performed to obtain the 100-yr design discharge and to prepare a continuous hydrograph for the sediment transport simulation. A hydraulic model of the crossing site was developed with U.S. Army Corps of Engineers computer program HEC-2 (U.S. Army Corps of Engineers, 1991), followed by sediment transport modeling with the Corps of Engineers sediment transport program HEC-6 (U.S. Army Corps of Engineers, 1993b; MacArthur et al., 1990). The results of the HEC-6 analysis were supplemented with empirical relationships for local scour and assessments of lateral channel stability. Other summaries of scour evaluation techniques employed at pipeline crossings can be found in Veldman (1983), Williams et al. (1992), and Yaremko and Cooper (1983).

Modeling sediment transport problems is not easy. Successful application is highly dependent on the professional experience and interpretation of the model user (Fan, 1994). The HEC-6 computer program was selected because it is one of the most widely used sediment transport programs in the United States. In addition, the authors of this chapter have the most experience with HEC-6. Author Williams has written some of the model's code

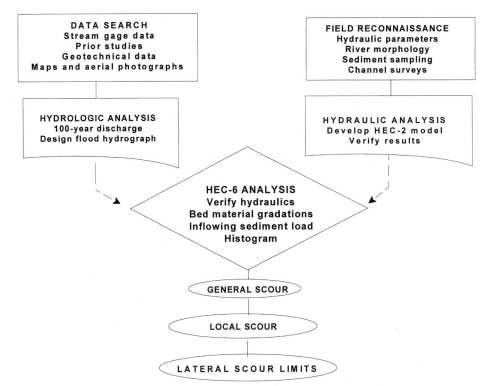

Figure 4. Flow chart of scour evaluation procedures.

channel. The overbank floodplain elevations were taken from the field surveys or from topographic maps. Figure 6 shows an example of surveyed channel cross sections used in the study. This figure also provides an indication of bed elevation changes that have occurred over time on the Gila River below Gillespie Dam. When previous cross-section geometry and flow records are available, this information can be used to calibrate the HEC-6 sediment transport model.

Sediment sampling. Bed material samples from the river channel were obtained at sites determined in the field by sedimentation engineers according to established guidelines (U.S. Army Corps of Engineers, 1989). Sampling sites were selected at locations that would provide information within the range of general and local scour depth anticipated for the design flood event. Samples were obtained from test pits dug by backhoe to a depth of about 3.7 m (12 ft). Borings were taken by EPNG along the pipeline alignment to a maximum depth of about 18.3 m (60 ft) to obtain information for pipeline construction. Sediment samples from the borings were also obtained. The number of test pits dug at each site ranged from six to 11; the number of borings excavated ranged from two to 18.

The bed material samples were analyzed in the laboratory for grain-size distribution using mechanical sieve analysis down to a fine sand size of 0.0625 mm (0.00246 in). Samples from borings were characterized and analyzed to determine depth of bedrock or strongly cemented and erosion-resistant soils. This information was helpful in determining trenching requirements for pipeline placement and the likely maximum

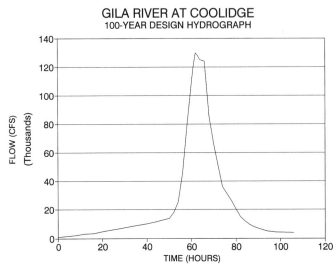

Figure 5. Example of 100-yr discharge design flood hydrograph.

depth of scour. The judgment of the sedimentation engineer was used to determine which samples to use as representative input to the HEC-6 model. Table 2 gives the range of median particle diameter and the depths from which these samples were obtained for the data used in the scour evaluations at the six pipeline crossing sites.

Only at the Gillespie Dam site on the Gila River was consolidated rock found within the depth of computed scour; however, it was not continuous across the river channel. Refraction

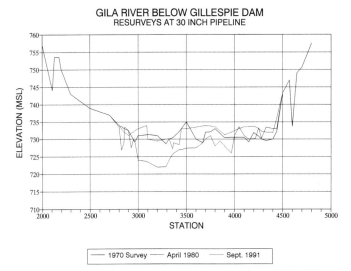

Figure 6. Example of surveyed channel cross sections and bed elevation changes over time along EPNG Line No. 1600.

TABLE 2. RANGE OF SEDIMENT DATA USED IN HEC-6

Location of Pipeline Crossing	Depth of Samples (m)	Median Diameter (mm)
Gila River at Gillespie Dam	0.6 to 4.6	13 to 18
Gila River at Coolidge	0.6 to 2.7	0.25 to 0.85
Gila River at Winkelman	1.2 to 1.5	7 to 20
Gila River at Duncan	0.3 to 2.4	1.5 to 5
Aravaipa Creek near Mammoth	1.2 to 2.1	3 to 12.5
San Pedro River at Mammoth	0.6 to 2.1	1.5 to 3.5

seismic analysis was used by EPNG to help determine the extent of the rock. At the other crossing sites, alluvial material was present to the maximum boring and sampling depth, except at Winkelman, where rock or erosion resistant material was found at about 10.7 m (35 ft).

Scour analysis. There are essentially two kinds of scour—general scour (or long-term degradation) and local scour (Pemberton and Lara, 1984). General scour is associated with streambed lowering over long periods of time during many flood events. It can be caused by depletion of upstream sediment sources, such as by deposition of sediment in reservoirs behind dams. Other factors that influence general scour include changes in stream gradient, changes in stream size and shape due to intrinsic hydraulic adjustments, human disturbances, and previous flood history. Local scour occurs during single flood events. It can be caused by a deepening incision of the low flow channel, flow constrictions between bridge abutments, flow concentration around stream bends, and impinging flows at stream confluences.

Determining the general scour part of the total scour requires information on the geometry of the stream upstream and downstream of the pipeline crossing. This information is used to develop hydraulic results such as flow depth, velocity, and flow width for each discharge of the design hydrograph. The sediment size gradation of the bed materials, the volume and composition of the sediment entering the reach for each discharge, and the flow rate and duration of each interval of the design hydrograph are also required. A long-term hydrograph can be reduced to a sediment-weighted histogram to reduce computation time (Williams and Bradley, 1990). The analysis of this information was conducted with the numerical sediment transport model, HEC-6. Of all the data required, the estimate of inflowing sediment load possibly held the most uncertainty. For this reason, scour sensitivities to inflowing sediment load were conducted, and conservative assumptions were used that leaned toward the computation of more rather than less scour. Yang's equation for sediment transport was used in the HEC-6 models.

The results of the HEC-6 simulation are for the most part representative of general scour. The model can, however, predict contraction scour due to the constriction of flow at bridge openings. Other local scour components must be added to the general scour to obtain the total scour. Analytical methods can be used to approximate local scour, such as the regime equations of Lacey and Blench (Pemberton and Lara, 1984). Lacey's regime scour equation was used in this study to establish the relationship between local scour and the mean depth of flow:

$$d_s = Z d_m \qquad (1)$$

where:
d_s = scour depth below streambed, feet
d_m = mean water depth, feet
Z = factor depending on stream characteristics as follows:

Stream Condition	*Z*
Straight reach	0.25
Moderate bend	0.50
Severe bend	0.75
Right angle bend	1.00
Vertical bank or wall	1.25

Lacey's method was selected over Blench's because Blench suggested that a Z value of 0.60 would apply in a reach without regard to whether it was straight, moderately bending, or severely bending. Another local scour component added was the scour depth due to formation of bed forms such as dunes or antidunes in the streambed. Generally, a scour depth due to bed forms was considered to be about one-quarter to one-half the flow depth. Information on bed forms can be found in the literature (Nordin and Algert, 1965; Yalin, 1964).

A lateral scour analysis, based upon historical aerial photographs and other site-specific information, was conducted in order to determine the maximum extent of pipe burial depth. River behavior and geomorphology were observed during field reconnaissance and analyzed from the aerial photographs. Historical channel meandering and lateral migration patterns were analyzed to estimate the probable lateral movement of the river near the pipeline crossing alignment. Meander belt width and activity were considered in the assessment of lateral migration of the alluvial channels. Several of the pipelines in this study failed as a result of meander migration or avulsion of the stream into previously less active or nonexistent channels.

The hydraulic parameters determined for the design flood, the computed depths of general and local scour, and the extent of lateral scour determined for each crossing site are shown in Table 3. With total scour depths approaching 9.1 m (30 ft) at some crossings, EPNG used an innovative construction technique to bury the pipeline in a narrow trench. The method is called "slurry trenching" and eliminates the need for large excavations and costly dewatering that would be required for conventional trenching in areas with a high water table. In the slurry trench method, a narrow trench 0.9 to 1.5 m (3 to 5 ft) wide is supported and stabilized with a high density bentonite clay and water slurry. The pipeline is either progressively lowered into the trench or floated and lowered entirely at one time (Carreon and Doeing, 1994).

GAS PIPELINE CROSSINGS

Figure 1 shows the locations of six stream crossing sites where EPNG pipelines failed or were exposed during the January 1993 flooding in Arizona. The site locations include the Gila River below Gillespie Dam, Gila River at Coolidge, Gila River at Winkelman, Gila River at Duncan, Aravaipa Creek near Mammoth, and San Pedro River at Mammoth. Some specific details pertinent to the scour evaluation at each crossing site are presented in the following sections.

Gila River at Gillespie Dam

Three EPNG natural gas pipelines cross the Gila River within 100 m (326 ft) downstream of Gillespie Dam below the old U.S. Route 80 highway bridge. Gillespie Dam was completed in the early 1920s for irrigation purposes. The dam is a free overflow concrete structure with an ogee crest approximately 6.1 m (20 ft) in height and about 520 m (1,700 ft) in length. There is a small

concrete stilling basin beneath the dam, and gates exist on each side of the river to release water to irrigation canals. The reservoir filled with sediment as a result of abundant upstream sediment supply within the first decade following construction. In fact, the elevation of the deposits in the reservoir immediately upstream of the dam have exceeded the elevation of the top of the dam by 0.6 m (2 ft). The Gila River drains 128,540 km^2 (49,650 mi^2) above Gillespie Dam.

The first EPNG pipeline downstream of the dam is the 76.2-cm (30-in) Line No. 1600, which was originally buried in 1969. The next two pipelines downstream are the 66-cm (26-in) Line No. 1100 and the 76.2-cm (30-in) Line No. 1103, which were buried in a common trench in 1992. Their burial depth was determined based upon a previous scour analysis that assumed the 100-yr design flood would overtop the entire width of Gillespie Dam. A failure of Gillespie Dam was not considered in the design flood criteria.

In 1993, a concrete section of Gillespie Dam about 46 m (150 ft) wide failed at 10:30 A.M. on January 9 (Figs. 7 and 8). The cause of the failure was not known. The peak flow before failure was estimated from a high water mark on the U.S. Geological Survey (USGS) gauge at the dam to be slightly greater than 5,700 cubic m per second (200,000 cfs). This flood peak corresponds to a 65-yr flood. The estimate by the U.S. Army Corps of Engineers for the 100-yr flood peak under existing conditions at this location is 6,700 cubic m per second (235,000 cfs) (U.S. Army Corps of Engineers, 1988). The maximum recorded discharge at the stream gauge in the period of record is 5,000 cubic m per second (178,000 cfs) on February 16, 1980.

EPNG Line No. 1600 ruptured January 11, 1993, after floating to the surface on January 9. The 1100 and 1103 lines failed shortly before midnight on January 19 during a subsequent flood with an estimate peak discharge of 5,100 cubic m per second (180,000 cfs). It is most likely that the maximum scour at these pipelines occurred during the peak of the first event or shortly thereafter. The pipelines were subjected to extreme stress and tremendous pressure differentials when they were exposed. Most likely, the failure of the 1100 and 1103 lines occurred because of

TABLE 3. HYDRAULIC DESIGN PARAMETERS AND RESULTS OF SCOUR ANALYSES

Pipeline Crossing	Slope (m/km)	100-Year Discharge (m³/s)	Top Width (m)	Maximum Velocity (m/sec)	Flow Depth (m)	General Scour (m)	Local Scour (m)	Bed Form Scour (m)	Maximum Vertical Scour (m)	Lateral Scour (m)
Gila River at Gillespie Dam	0.23	6,600	90	9.8	5.4	4.2	2.7	1.2	8.1	1,200
Gila River at Coolidge	0.34	3,700	460	4.7	3.8	1.9	2.2	0.9	5.0	2,050
Gila River at Winkelman	1.7	3,400	450	2.8	7.6	1.5	5.7	....	7.2	1,650
Gila River at Duncan	0.19	1,070	170	4.3	4.7	1.9	2.4	0.6	4.9	460
Aravaipa Creek near Mammoth	0.21	800	200	3.4	1.7	0.2	0.9	0.6	1.7	900
San Pedro River at Mammoth	0.17	1,300	190	4.6	3.0	1.7	2.3	0.6	4.6	650

Figure 7. Gila River at Gillespie Dam: aerial view looking downstream through dam on January 21, 1993, with estimated flow rate of 2,000 cubic m per second (70,000 cfs), photograph from U.S. Army Corps of Engineers.

Figure 8. Gila River at Gillespie Dam: view of flow through dam breach on January 20, 1993. Photograph by B. Doeing.

vortex shedding and severe oscillation of the pipes. These two pipelines did not float prior to failure because they were anchored by concrete blocks poured every 100 m (326 ft). The 1600 line was not anchored as strongly and hence floated when exposed.

The breach in the dam acted to concentrate flow over the pipelines to an effective flow width of about 91 m (300 ft) at the 1100 and 1103 crossing. Surface wave patterns that indicated the presence of antidunes were observed by the authors in this area on the day after the failure of the 1100 and 1103 lines. Based on the surface wave height, amplitudes of 1.5 to 2.4 m (5 to 8 ft) from crest to trough were estimated for the antidunes in the river bed. Antidunes are a bed form indicative of critical or supercritical flow. Based on these observations and later confirmed with the HEC-6 sediment transport model, the maximum velocity at the pipelines as a result of the focused flow was approximately 9.1 m (30 ft) per second. The maximum velocity that would be expected if the dam had simply been overtopped without failure is approximately 3.8 m (12.5 ft) per second.

The earlier analysis of the 1100 and 1103 lines was based on an HEC-2 model originally prepared by the U.S. Army Corps of Engineers for a 1988 flood insurance study for Maricopa County. This model was supplemented with channel geometry based on 1991 topographic surveys. Survey data obtained by EPNG along the 1600 pipeline alignment during 1970, 1980, and 1991 provide an indication of bed elevation changes over time (Fig. 6). This information was used to calibrate the HEC-6 model.

The general scour computed by HEC-6 for the design flood was equal to 4.2 m (13.7 ft). The flow depth at peak discharge was 5.4 m (17.8 ft). Using Lacey's relation of 50% of flow depth for local scour in a moderate bend resulted in a local scour of 2.7 m (8.9 ft). With 1.2 m (4 ft) added for the formation of antidunes, the maximum potential scour is 8.1 m (26.6 ft).

Gila River at Coolidge

The 15.2-cm (6-in) EPNG Line No. 2026 gas pipeline crossing the Gila River near Coolidge ruptured after the January 6–8 storm. This crossing is approximately 40 km (25 mi) downstream of the USGS stream gauge on the Gila River at Kelvin; however, no major tributaries enter between Kelvin and the pipeline crossing. The Gila River drains 46,630 km^2 (18,011 mi^2) above Kelvin, of which 13,269 km^2 (5,125 mi^2) are below Coolidge Dam. A provisional peak flow at Kelvin was estimated by the USGS to be 1,400 cubic m per second (50,000 cfs) on January 9, 1993, corresponding to a flow discharge slightly greater than the 25-yr flood (Roeske, 1978). The estimate of the 100-yr flood at Coolidge used in the scour evaluation was 3,700 cubic m per second (130,000 cfs). The hydrograph for this flood was developed by increasing the ordinates of the 1,400-cubic m per second (50,000-cfs) hydrograph at Kelvin by the ratio of the 100-yr peak flow to the peak flow of 1,400 cubic m per second (50,000 cfs) (Fig. 5).

Complications causing great changes in actual stream location during the January 1993 flood include failure of the north and south abutments of the Attaway Road bridge upstream of the pipeline crossing (Fig. 9) and a chute cutoff of a meander immediately upstream of Attaway Road. Maximum scour depths at the pipeline were probably not extreme because of the great width of the channel and the floodplain during peak flows, but the channel shifted laterally over 600 m (2,000 ft) during the flood. A meander belt is evident at this crossing, with an estimated width between 1,500 and 1,800 m (5,000 and 6,000 ft). It provides evidence that the stream channel migrated significantly during previous floods. Failure of the pipeline resulted from this lateral shift in the channel, which undercut the pipe in an overbank area where pipeline burial depth was more shallow (Fig. 10).

The 2026 line crosses the Gila River at a skew angle of about 45°. For this reason, the hydraulic parameters and computed scour depths vary along the pipeline alignment. The maximum computed values are listed in Table 3. Inspection of the table also shows that this crossing has the highest potential lateral extent of scour (2,050 m [6,700 ft]) of all the crossing sites evaluated.

Gila River at Winkelman

Three EPNG natural gas pipelines cross the Gila River at Winkelman, just upstream of the confluence with the San Pedro River. These include the 15.2-cm (6-in) Line No. 2023, the 21.9-cm (8.625-in) Line No. 2139, and the 16.8-cm (6.625-in) Line No. 2071. The 2139 line was an aerial crossing, and the other two lines were buried. The 2139 line failed when the bridge carrying the pipeline collapsed following the loss of bridge piers. The other two lines were exposed in a number of areas. The Gila River drains 34,351 km² (13,268 mi²) above Winkelman, of which 989 km² (382 mi²) are below Coolidge Dam.

Coolidge Dam regulates flow in the Gila River upstream of this crossing site. Although the maximum regulated release is 133 cubic m per second (4,700 cfs), the maximum outflow from the dam during the January 1993 storm was 927 cubic m per second (32,750 cfs) on January 20 and 21. This flow rate is between

Figure 10. Gila River at Coolidge: view of pipeline exposed at cut bank on north side of river on March 1, 1993. Photograph by B. Doeing.

a 25- and 50-yr flood for the river (Roeske, 1978) and is the highest discharge released from the dam since its completion in 1928. The river exits a narrow canyon approximately 1.6 to 3.2 km (1 to 2 mi) upstream of the site. The main channel through this reach has a bank-full capacity on the order of 140 cubic m per second (5,000 cfs). At higher flows, flood waters inundate the right overbank, which sits on a bench below the bluff where the town of Winkelman is located. The pipelines cross several hundred meters of the overbank area and pass through a residential portion of Winkelman called Winkelman Flats.

The maximum discharge recorded at Winkelman during the 1993 flooding was 1,050 cubic m per second (37,200 cfs) on January 20. The flood water inundated the overbank areas and reached an elevation above the roofs of some of the homes in Winkelman Flats. Velocities were visually approximated in excess of 2.1 m (7 ft) per second through this area as a result of high gradients and secondary flows around the homes and through the streets. Upstream of the housing development, the flow filled an old oxbow channel and caused significant lateral migration of this old channel. All of the pipelines were exposed throughout the overbank area as a result of either lateral migration of the old oxbow channel or local scour throughout Winkelman Flats (Fig. 11).

At the time of the scour evaluations, Coolidge dam was maintaining flows at 120 cubic m per second (4,200 cfs), near the maximum controlled outflow. These near-bank-full flows at Winkelman precluded taking field surveys in the channel or obtaining sediment samples. A 1979 flood insurance study for the Gila River at Winkelman had been performed by the USGS. Because of the short time frame available for completion of this study as well as the anticipated continued high releases from Coolidge Dam, it was decided to utilize the hydraulics from the previous FEMA study to conduct the scour assessment. It also appeared, based upon field reconnaissance, that the main channel had changed little since the FEMA study for the design scenario of the 100-yr flood with a peak discharge of 3,400 cubic

Figure 9. Gila River at Coolidge: south abutment of Attaway Road bridge on January 21, 1993. Photograph by B. Doeing.

Figure 11. Gila River at Winkelman: view of pipelines exposed in overbank area at Winkelman Flats on February 10, 1993. Photograph by B. Doeing.

m per second (120,000 cfs). The cross sections from the FEMA microfiche records were digitized and input into HEC-2 format, and a new hydraulic model was developed.

Even though a detailed general scour analysis was not conducted, it was possible to make an analytical assessment based on site-specific geomorphology and the river hydraulics. The Gila River, as previously described, exits a narrow canyon 1.6 to 3.2 km (1 to 2 mi) upstream of the pipeline crossing. The valley then widens extensively, the gradient flattens, and moderate to higher flows go overbank through the area of Winkelman Flats. The river is again confined about 335 m (1,100 ft) downstream of the pipeline crossing at a highway bridge. The flatter gradient at the pipeline crossing and the backwater effect of the bridge reduce the flow velocity below that of the cross sections upstream. The crossing area is therefore either a sediment deposition or transport zone, and general scour should be limited. Accordingly, a conservative general scour of 1.5 m (5 ft) was assumed for the design event in the main channel.

A conservative local scour of 75% of the flow depth was assumed based on the pipeline crossing location in a severe bend. No additional scour for bed forms was applied. Using the hydraulics computed from the HEC-2 model, local scour was computed as 5.7 m (18.6 ft). Adding this to the general scour of 1.5 m (5 ft) resulted in a total potential scour of 7.2 m (23.6 ft) beneath the channel bottom.

Gila River at Duncan

Just downstream of Duncan, Arizona, two EPNG natural gas pipelines cross the Gila River. EPNG Line No. 2006 and Line No. 2007 are both 16.8-cm (6.625-in) diameter. The crossing location is in a meander bend with a historical meander belt width in excess of 600 m (2,000 ft). As a result of the extreme flows in January 1993, the channel migrated laterally and caused failure of the pipelines. The failure occurred in an overbank area where the pipe burial depth was not as deep as in the channel. Although both lines

failed on January 19, 1993, they probably were initially exposed on January 11, when the peak flow on the Gila River below Blue Creek near Virden, New Mexico (about 32 km [20 mi] upstream), was 850 cubic m per second (30,000 cfs).

The Gila River at the gauge near Virden has a drainage area of 8,293 km² (3,203 mi²). The 100-yr peak flow at the Virden gage is 1,070 cubic m per second (37,900 cfs) (Garrett and Gellenbeck, 1991). The design hydrograph for Duncan was obtained by increasing the peak flow in the 1993 hydrograph at Virden to 1,070 cubic m per second (37,900 cfs). Twelve cross sections were surveyed across the river and input into an HEC-2 model. General scour at the crossing was computed with HEC-6 to be 1.9 m (6.2 ft). With a flow depth of 4.7 m (15.4 ft) and using Lacey's "Z" factor of 0.50 for a moderate bend, a local scour of 2.4 m (7.7 ft) was calculated. Adding to this an additional 0.6 m (2 ft) to account for the possible presence of antidunes resulted in a total potential scour of 4.9 m (15.9 ft) below the channel bottom. To avoid exposure due to possible lateral migration of the channel, the maximum burial depth was recommended to extend for a width of 460 m (1,500 ft) at the crossing.

Aravaipa Creek near Mammoth

The 16.8-cm (6.625-in) EPNG Line No. 2071 natural gas pipeline crossing Aravaipa Creek was exposed on January 8, 1993, but it did not fail during the January storms. The highest discharges recorded by the USGS gauge on Aravaipa Creek near Mammoth in 1993 were 220 cubic m per second (7,800 cfs) on January 8 and 370 cubic m per second (13,000 cfs) on January 11. A discharge of 230 cubic m per second (8,000 cfs) has a recurrence interval of 5 years based upon a log-Pearson Type III analysis. The drainage area upstream of this site is only 1,390 km² (537 mi²) but has historically produced extremely large floods. The peak discharge of record, 2,000 cubic m per second (70,800 cfs), occurred on October 1, 1983. The 100-yr design discharge of 800 cubic m per second (28,200 cfs) was obtained from an analysis of the stream gauge record (U.S. Geological Survey, 1989).

The main channel scoured during the event but not to such a depth that the line was exposed. The pipeline exposure occurred in what had previously been a farmer's field in the left overbank, looking downstream. A secondary channel, about 60 m (200 ft) in width, was created through the farmer's field as a result of an upstream avulsion. The area where the pipeline was exposed was not previously an active portion of the Aravaipa Creek channel. The initial data search did not uncover a previous hydraulic model. Thirteen surveyed cross sections were obtained about 90 to 150 m (300 to 500 ft) apart, and the data were input into HEC-2.

The general scour computed by HEC-6 was 0.2 m (0.6 ft). This seemingly low value is due to the hydraulics of flow at the crossing site and the coarse nature of the bed materials. The pipeline crossing is in an area of expanding flow in a very wide stream. The effective flow width in the study reach varies from about 240 m (800 ft) upstream of the crossing to about 370 m (1,200 ft) below. The large effective flow width and the low depth of flow (1.7 m [5.6 ft]) act to minimize development of large tractive forces on the channel bottom. However, inspection of the model output indicates that although sediment transport capacity for smaller grain sizes exists at peak flow, the finer sediments are protected by an armor layer of coarse materials. This armor layer develops through hydraulic sorting of the bed materials.

With a general scour of 0.2 m (0.6 ft), a local scour of 0.9 m (2.8 ft) based on Lacey's relation of 50% of flow depth for a moderate bend, and allowing 0.6 m (2 ft) for the formation of dunes or antidunes, a total scour of 1.7 m (5.4 ft) was obtained. Because the channel has shown the tendency to migrate into areas where sediment samples were not obtained, a greater design scour depth was recommended. This design depth ranged from 2.4 to 4.6 m (8 to 15 ft), depending on the location of the pipeline within the active meander belt, which has a width of 900 m (2,950 ft).

San Pedro River at Mammoth

The 16.8-cm (6.625-in) EPNG Line No. 2071 crosses the San Pedro River several hundred meters downstream of State Highway 77 bridge at Mammoth. The pipeline had spanned the river on a truss bridge supported by piers of pile bents. Piles connected with chains, acting as debris collectors, were located immediately upstream of some of the bridge piers. The debris collectors were installed by EPNG to minimize debris buildup on the bridge piers (Fig. 12). An additional measure installed by EPNG to protect the bridge was a series of pile dikes placed on the outside of the bend along the right bank of the river between the highway and the pipeline bridge. The purpose of the pile dikes was to induce sediment deposition and minimize lateral stream migration.

On January 8, 1993, a bridge pier failed, and a section of the bridge truss collapsed. The peak flow recorded on January 8 at the USGS gauge near Redington, Arizona, about 32 km (20 mi) upstream, was 425 cubic m per second (15,000 cfs). The San Pedro River near Redington drains an area of

Figure 12. San Pedro River at Mammoth: view of pipeline truss bridge and debris collectors on January 21, 1993. Photograph by B. Doeing.

7,578 km² (2,927 mi²). Prior to this flood, the main channel had flowed around an island immediately downstream of the pipeline crossing. In January 1993, the island was eliminated, and the main channel shifted from the left to the right side of the crossing site. Large amounts of tamarisk are found in the watershed and large amounts of woody debris are therefore transported in the river. A significant amount of woody debris was observed on the piers of the highway bridge after the flood. The pier that failed at the gas line crossing was the only one not protected with a debris collector. It is most likely that the buildup of debris on the pier increased its effective area and enhanced local pier scour. Principles involved in determining pier scour at bridges can be found in Federal Highway Administration (1993). EPNG elected to replace the pipeline bridge crossing with a buried crossing.

Fourteen surveyed channel cross sections at a spacing of 90 to 150 m (300 to 500 ft) were obtained for the scour evaluation study and were used as input for an HEC-2 model. The 100-yr design peak flow of 1,325 cubic m per second (46,800 cfs) was obtained from a 1990 FEMA flood insurance study completed for Pinal County. The HEC-2 results were compared with the published results of the 1990 flood insurance study for reasonableness. The general scour computed with HEC-6 for the design flood was equal to 1.7 m (5.4 ft). The flow depth at peak discharge was 3.0 m (9.9 ft). Using Lacey's criteria of 75% of the flow depth in a severe bend results in 2.3 m (7.4 ft) for local scour. With the addition of 0.6 m (2 ft) for the possible formation of antidunes, the total estimated scour is 4.6 m (14.8 ft).

The lateral limit of scour in the right overbank is influenced by the State Highway 77 bridge upstream, which forms a control point. The orientation of the bridge opening and the momentum of flow direct the river to the north. In the January 1993 floods, a new secondary channel was eroded behind the pile jetties on the right bank. Considering the low right overbank elevations and the indications of historical channel patterns on the aerial photographs, an expansion of flow from the bridge opening was used to estimate the limits of scour in the right overbank. A natural expansion, 1.2 m (4 ft) longitudinal to 0.3 m (1 ft) lateral, was used to model the flow.

The limit for scour in the left overbank is influenced by the berms of water treatment ponds that exist on the left bank upstream of the pipeline. Although it is unlikely that the main channel could migrate to the left downstream of the water treatment ponds, secondary flows may develop in this area. Under some conditions, these secondary flows may accelerate to velocities in excess of the main channel velocity. The left limit for maximum scour was therefore set back beyond the location where secondary flows would form. In sum, the lateral limits of maximum scour potential were estimated to extend a total of 670 m (2,200 ft) at the pipeline crossing.

SUMMARY

This chapter presents a case study that demonstrates the effects of the 1992–1993 storms on six EPNG natural gas pipelines that cross streams in the Gila River Basin in southern and central Arizona. Some of the pipelines were buried, and some were carried across the streams on bridges. Specific meteorologic and hydrologic conditions were responsible for the floods. Sediment transport and scour phenomenan led to exposure or failure of the pipelines. Because it was extremely important for these lines to be replaced as soon as possible, detailed scour evaluations were conducted to determine the maximum scour and the lateral extent of scour for the 100-yr design flood. These results were used in the design, construction, and permitting process to expedite replacement or repair of the pipelines.

One significant aspect of this account is that the investigations uncovered a number of potential hazards in the river environment to pipelines or other manmade structures. Failures were caused not only by vertical scour of the streambed but also by bank erosion, lateral channel migration, avulsions, bridge scour, and secondary flows outside the main channel. The scour evaluation techniques considered these potential hazards in the determination of maximum scour and lateral limits for scour. The studies show that the minimum cover required by pipeline safety regulations may not be adequate for the intended design life of the pipeline.

The studies also show that the problems related to flooding, erosion, and damages to pipelines are recognizable and, to a certain extent, predictable and preventable. A cost/benefit study for both new and existing installations may easily prove that this type of analysis, followed by good engineering design, could reduce losses with a cost/benefit favoring the analysis.

Finally, in the replacement or repair of these pipelines, a new construction approach was used by EPNG to excavate the pipe trenches. The technique, called "slurry trenching," saved the company both time and money. With this method, a narrow trench supported by a bentonite clay and water slurry minimizes excavation quantities and eliminates the need for dewatering. The availability of this method should encourage pipeline operators to evaluate the maximum depth of potential scour for design conditions and bury new pipelines accordingly.

ACKNOWLEDGMENTS

The authors wish to acknowledge those persons who were instrumental in the successful completion of the studies described in this chapter. Samuel Carreon, Jr., EPNG, provided the overall technical supervision. Norman Wetz, SHB-AGRA, supplied geotechnical information from field-sediment samples. Joseph Evelyn, U.S. Army Corps of Engineers, Los Angeles District, provided reservoir operations data for Painted Rock Dam and aerial photographs of the Gila River. Robert Wallace and staff members at the U.S. Geological Survey offices in Tempe and Tucson, Arizona, supplied historical and current stream-flow data. Dallas Reigle, Salt River Project, and Bethany Barron, U.S. Bureau of Reclamation, provided reservoir flow release data.

REFERENCES CITED

Carreon, S., and Doeing, B. J., 1994, Slurry trenching for waterway pipeline installation, *in* Proceedings, Hydraulics of Pipelines, Phoenix, Arizona: New York, American Society of Civil Engineers, Pipeline Division, p. 261–279.

Chang, H. H., 1988, Fluvial processes in river engineering: New York, John Wiley & Sons, 432 p.

Fan, Shou-shan, ed., 1988, Twelve selected computer stream sedimentation models developed in the United States: Washington, D.C., Interagency Sedimentation Work Group Report, 552 p.

Fan, Shou-shan, 1994, An interagency overview of selected stream sedimentation models, *in* Proceedings, Hydraulic Engineering '94, Buffalo, New York: New York, American Society of Civil Engineers, Hydraulics Division, p. 1166–1170.

Federal Highway Administration (FHWA), Office of Research and Development, 1993, Evaluating scour at bridges (second edition): Washington, D.C., Hydraulic Engineering Circular 18, FHWA-IP90-017, 132 p.

Garrett, J. M., and Gellenbeck, D. J., 1991, Basin characteristics and streamflow statistics in Arizona as of 1989: U.S. Geological Survey Water-Resources Investigations Report 91-4041, 612 p.

MacArthur, R. C., Williams, D. T., and Thomas, W. A., 1990, Status and new capabilities of computer program HEC-6: Scour and deposition in rivers and reservoirs, *in* Proceedings, Hydraulic Engineering, San Diego, California: New York, American Society of Civil Engineers, Hydraulics Division, p. 475–480.

MacNish, R. D., Smith, C. F., and Goddard, K. E., 1993, Floods in Arizona, January 1993: U.S. Geological Survey Open-File Report 93-54, 2 p.

National Oceanic and Atmospheric Administration (NOAA), National Weather Service, 1981, The disastrous southern California and central Arizona floods, flash floods, and mudslides of February 1980: Natural Disaster Survey Report NWS-81-1, 70 p.

Nordin, C., and Algert, J. A., 1965, Geometric properties of sand waves: Discussion, *in* Proceedings, American Society of Civil Engineers, v. 91, no. HY5.

Pemberton, E. L., and Lara, J. M., 1984, Computing degradation and local scour: Technical guideline for Bureau of Reclamation: Denver, Colorado, Bureau of Reclamation, 48 p.

Ponce, V. M., Ozmoiski, Z., and Smutzer, D., 1985, Large basin deterministic hydrology: A case study: American Society of Civil Engineers, Journal of Hydraulic Engineering, v. 111, p. 1227–1245.

Roeske, R. H., 1978, Methods for estimating the magnitude and frequency of floods in Arizona: Arizona Department of Transportation Report ADOT-RS-15-121, 82 p.

Smith, C. F., Rigas, P. D., Ham, L. K., Duet, N. R., and Anning, D. W., 1994, Water resources data, Arizona, water year 1993: U.S. Geological Survey Water-Data Report AZ 93-1, 360 p.

Thomas, B. E., Hjalmarson, H. W., and Waltemayer, S. D., 1994, Methods for estimating magnitude and frequency of floods in the southwestern United States: U.S. Geological Survey Open-File Report 93-419, 211 p.

U.S. Army Corps of Engineers (USACE), Los Angeles District, 1954, Design memorandum no. 1, hydrology for Painted Rock Reservoir, Gila River, Arizona: Los Angeles, California, U.S. Army Corps of Engineers, 36 p.

U.S. Army Corps of Engineers (USACE), Los Angeles District, 1988, Study for flood control, alternatives to Cliff Dam: Los Angeles, California, U.S. Army Corps of Engineers, 62 p.

U.S. Army Corps of Engineers (USACE), 1989, Sedimentation investigations of rivers and reservoirs: Washington, D.C., U.S. Army Corps of Engineers, Engineer Manual EM 1110-2-4000, 76 p.

U.S. Army Corps of Engineers (USACE), Hydrologic Engineering Center, 1991, HEC-2, Water surface profiles, user's manual: Davis, California, U.S. Army Corps of Engineers, 47 p.

U.S. Army Corps of Engineers (USACE), Hydrologic Engineering Center, 1992, HEC-FFA, Flood frequency analysis, user's manual: Davis, California, U.S. Army Corps of Engineers, 75 p.

U.S. Army Corps of Engineers (USACE), Los Angeles District, 1993a, 1993

Gila River floods and Painted Rock Dam operations: videotape.

U.S. Army Corps of Engineers (USACE), Hydrologic Engineering Center, 1993b, HEC-6, Scour and deposition in rivers and reservoirs, user's manual: Davis, California, U.S. Army Corps of Engineers, 164 p.

U.S. Department of Transportation (USDOT), Research and Special Programs Administration, 1994, Pipeline safety regulations, part 190-199: Washington, D.C., U.S. Department of Transportation, p. 351–534.

U.S. Geological Survey (USGS), 1989, Basin characteristics and streamflow statistics in Arizona as of 1989: Washington, D.C., U.S. Geological Survey, Water Resources Investigations Report 91-4041, 612 p.

U.S. Water Resources Council (USWRC), 1981, Guidelines for determining flood flow frequency: Washington, D.C., Bulletin 17B, 171 p.

Veldman, W. M., 1983, Arctic pipeline river crossings—design trends and lessons learned, *in* Proceedings, Pipelines in Adverse Environments II, San Diego, California: New York, American Society of Civil Engineers, Pipeline Division, p. 70–83.

Williams, D. T., and Bradley, J. B., 1990, The sediment weighted histogram generator and estimation of sediment transport trends, *in* Proceedings, Hydraulic Engineering, San Diego, California: New York, American Society of Civil Engineers, Hydraulics Division, p. 378–384.

Williams, D. T., Carreon, S., and Bradley, J. B., 1992, Evaluation of erosion potential at pipeline crossings, *in* Proceedings, Water Forum '92, Baltimore, Maryland: New York, American Society of Civil Engineers, Hydraulics Division, p. 689–694.

Yalin, M. S., 1964, Geometric properties of sand waves, *in* Proceedings, American Society of Civil Engineers, v. 90, no. HY5.

Yaremko, E. K., and Cooper, R. H., 1983, Influence of northern pipelines on river crossing design, *in* Proceedings, Pipelines in Adverse Environments II, San Diego, California: New York, American Society of Civil Engineers, Pipeline Division, p. 49–63.

MANUSCRIPT ACCEPTED BY THE SOCIETY JANUARY 29, 1997

Geological Society of America
Reviews in Engineering Geology, Volume XI
1997

Channel adjustments from instream mining:
San Luis Rey River, San Diego County, California

Michael Sandecki
California Department of Conservation, Office of Mine Reclamation, 801 K Street, Sacramento, California 95814
Catherine Crossett Avila
California Department of Transportation, 1891 Alhambra Boulevard, Sacramento, California 95816

ABSTRACT

The San Luis Rey River comprises a 1,450-km^2 (560-mi^2) watershed in northern San Diego County, California. Construction aggregate has been mined along a 22.5-km (14-mi) reach of the river. Cumulative extraction volumes of eight operators peaked in the late 1980s, with few restrictions or coordinated oversight by local, state, or federal agencies. The river channel was deepened and widened as sand was removed at rates far in excess of natural replenishment. The 1992–1993 floods caused headward erosion of the mined pit boundaries, interruption of sediment transport continuity, and downstream scour. Lowering the base level in the mined portions triggered rapid erosional adjustments in nonmined portions of the river, affecting infrastructure, adjacent property, and wildlife habitat. During the 1992–1993 storms, the riverbed degraded 2.4 to 3.7 m (8 to 12 ft) under the old Route 395 bridge, causing structural instability that closed the bridge to traffic and necessitated a $4.5 million bridge replacement project. The Route 76 bridge over a tributary to the San Luis Rey River failed as the tributary headcut upstream, lowering the bed in the mainstem. The exposure of aqueduct crossings, sewage lines, natural gas conduits, and bridge foundations prompted a comprehensive evaluation of instream mining activity, initiated by the San Diego County Water Authority in 1990. Concurrently, the Environmental Protection Agency authorized funding a watershed management plan to preserve or replace habitat critical to rare, threatened, and endangered species. The lessons learned from the San Luis Rey River include: (1) the cumulative impacts of sand removal should be quantified, and potential offsite impact areas identified; (2) the effects of bed lowering on infrastructure can be quantified and used to limit mining depths and locations; and (3) the loss of riparian habitat can be minimized by identifying affected areas, preserving critical areas, and promptly implementing aquatic habitat and wildlife enhancement programs to restore impacted areas.

INTRODUCTION

In California, construction aggregate is often mined from recent river channel deposits. Sand-bedded rivers, such as the San Luis Rey, supply a clean, well-graded aggregate product. Aggregate operators prefer sites that are located in river channels because the floodplain's active nature prevents the development of overburden and can wash away vegetation that might otherwise become established on the floodplain. Flooding can obliterate excavation boundaries and bring in fresh material, precluding the need to relocate an operation.

Northern San Diego County has been "undergoing rapid

Sandecki, M., and Avila, C. C., 1997, Channel adjustments from instream mining: San Luis Rey River, San Diego County, California, *in* Larson, R. A., and Slosson, J. E., eds., Storm-Induced Geologic Hazards: Case Histories from the 1992–1993 Winter in Southern California and Arizona: Boulder, Colorado, Geological Society of America Reviews in Engineering Geology, v. XI.

urbanization," creating a demand for high quality, Portland Cement Concrete (PCC) aggregate. The importance of the aggregate resource in the San Luis Rey River and floodplain to regional growth was documented in a Mineral Land Classification report completed by the California Division of Mines and Geology (1983).

The physical changes to a river resulting from aggregate removal were explored by only a few planning agencies prior to the 1980s. The complexity of river processes and lack of data plagued river planning efforts. Basic scientific principles, however, can be applied by management agencies to address riverbed mining. The application of these principles to mining activities on the San Luis Rey River is the subject of this chapter.

The first of these physical principles is sediment supply. In this chapter, we categorize rivers as aggrading, degrading, or stable over the long term. These terms describe the loss or gain of bed material (sand and gravel) over a period of time and the consequent raising or lowering of the bed elevation. The balance between the sediment supply and the channel's ability to transport sediment is manifested in bed elevation trends. Aggrading rivers are those in which the bed elevation is rising with a buildup of material in the channel. This condition persists when the sediment load exceeds the transport capacity of the channel. Degrading rivers show the opposite trend: The bed elevation becomes lower over time. The relationship between overexcavation and degradation is particularly dynamic in an alluvial river, which scours its bed and banks to reach a balance between supply and transport.

An aggrading river condition is generally a result of a rapidly eroding watershed. Rapid erosion may be a product of land use practices, tectonic uplift, weak bedrock geology, vegetation loss to fire, or a combination of these factors. A degrading river condition is a function of sediment transport capacity in excess of sediment supply. Where the sediment supply is less than the sediment transporting ability of a river, the river picks up material stored in the channel bed or banks, hence, a degradational trend or lateral erosion may occur. Mining of bed material in excess of replenishment increases the size of a channel and also may result in channel degradation.

Sediment transport theory is crucial to understanding river behavior. Sediment transport is analogous to a conveyor belt moving manufactured goods (Kondolf, 1993). Sediment is conveyed along the river "belt," which runs from the upper watershed to the ocean (or other topographic lowpoint). The conveyor runs only during flood events. Some channel segments or reaches are more efficient conveyors, transporting more material and storing little, whereas others are less efficient and act as sediment sinks or traps. The differences in transport rates can be attributed to geomorphological changes or to human modifications such as mining excavations and channelization. When differences in transport rates are coupled with the variations in sediment production from watershed erosion, complex patterns of sediment distribution occur. The intensity and duration of storm events control the amount of material moved into the system and trans-

ported by the conveyor. Generally, larger storms increase erosion and transport greater sediment volumes.

Dams can influence the sediment balance and transport characteristics of a river system. The water storage dam at Lake Henshaw, for example, is a catchment for about a third of the total watershed area of the San Luis Rey River. Consequently, at least a third of the watershed's sediment load has been eliminated as a source of replenishment since 1923. Dams raise the base level of the channel above the dam by increasing the elevation of the water surface in the impoundment pool. Raising the base level decreases the energy of the flow and reduces hydraulic efficiency, causing sand and gravel (bed material load) and most finer material (suspended load) to be deposited into the reservoir. This upstream deposition behind the dam causes degradation downstream, since the water exiting the dam is generally sediment starved "clear water." This "hungry water" exiting the dam picks up sediment downstream of the dam, because it has excess energy to expend and "eats" at the bed and banks to restore the sediment transport energy to an equilibrium condition.

SETTING

The San Luis Rey River drains a 1,443-km^2 (557-mi^2) watershed, with its headwaters at Palomar Mountain (elevation 1,740 m [5,710 ft]) and outfall at the Pacific Ocean in the City of Oceanside (Fig. 1). The watershed consists of mainly unimproved land supporting coastal sage scrub at lower elevations, mixed conifer forest at higher elevations, and riparian areas along the river corridor. The completion of the Lake Henshaw dam in 1923 diminished flood peaks in the lower basin and diminished downstream sediment supply.

The maximum discharge recorded on the San Luis River occurred in 1916, prior to the completion of Henshaw Dam, when 2,707 cubic m per second (95,600 cubic feet per second [cfs]) was recorded near the river's mouth at the Oceanside gauge (#11042000). Since dam completion, the highest discharge at the same gauge was 728 cubic m per second (25,700 cfs), resulting from 17.27 cm (6.80 in) of rain falling in a 24-hr period, as recorded on the Santa Rosa Plateau on January 16, 1993. During a 2-month period in 1993, the San Luis Rey basin recorded approximately 200% of its average annual rainfall (Bowers, 1993).

Below Henshaw Dam, the river flows through rocky canyons and steep alluvial fans for several kilometers before traversing a series of broad alluvial basins that extend to the Pacific Ocean. Dry farming, livestock grazing, and other development have occurred on the floodplain and valley floor along the lower 32-km (20-mi) reach, and considerable urbanization is present, especially near the City of Oceanside. Riparian areas line the river corridor but are displaced by infrastructure, mining activities, farming, and urban development. Riparian areas are home to the least Bell's vireo (*Vireo bellii pusillus*), an endemic bird with federal and state endangered species status.

In the lower 32-km (20-mi) reach, flood control channelization projects and extensive sand mining have occurred, which have altered the riverbed and changed sediment transport char-

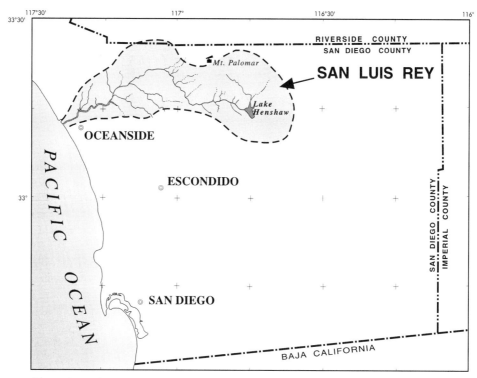

Figure 1. The San Luis Rey watershed is located in northern San Diego County, California.

acteristics. The lower reach contains multiple river crossings for highways and utilities, including two aqueducts that import 90% of San Diego County's water supply.

WATERSHED SEDIMENT PRODUCTION

The amount of sediment transported at any point in the system (sediment yield) is limited to the amount produced in the watershed plus eroded material from the channel bed and banks. Watershed sediment production is important in aggregate mining management because it represents the volume of aggregate material available to replenish a site during significant discharges. When mining extraction volumes exceed sediment yield, the river is unable to replenish the excavation, resulting in an enlarged or deepened channel. When mining extraction equals the sediment yield, bed and bank erosion are minimized.

A sediment budget is helpful in evaluating the balance between watershed sediment production and cumulative mining extraction volumes (Collins and Dunne, 1990). A sediment budget is produced by first estimating a watershed sediment production volume. The volume added or removed from storage (mined or transported volume) in the river reach for which the budget is prepared is then assessed. Combining the change in storage with watershed production will yield the volume of sediment passed completely through the river. Where one can assess two of the three volumes, the third unknown can be estimated. The sediment budget provides an order-of-magnitude estimate that can be used to prescribe extraction volumes that will keep the system in balance until fine tuning can be accomplished.

Detailed studies on sediment yield and replenishment to mining areas are not available for the San Luis Rey basin. In fact, because mining extraction volumes are considered proprietary, exact extraction figures are unavailable. Lettieri, McIntyre and Associates, Inc. (1995), however, estimated average bedload yield below Lake Henshaw at 87,054 metric tons/yr (97,500 tons/yr). They also estimated delivery of sediment to the coast at 19,643 metric tons/yr (22,000 tons/yr)—this included natural sediment replenishment less the amount trapped by Lake Henshaw. Therefore, an average of about 67,411 metric tons/yr (75,500 tons/yr) (38,485 cubic meters/yr or 50,333 cubic yards/yr) was available for mining (aggraded or stored) in the intervening reach. Their estimate is based on reservoir sedimentation rates, and the values are extrapolated to the drainage area of the San Luis Rey River below the dam. Comparison of this sediment budget to excavated aggregate volumes indicates that extraction of material on the San Luis Rey River far exceeded deposition in the reach as well as supply from the watershed. Mining records indicate a single operator removed more aggregate than is estimated in the above sediment budget. The eight operators combined removed a volume of aggregate greatly in excess of that available, as suggested by the sediment budget. This conclusion, however, cannot be quantified, since a record of mine production volumes is unavailable.

CHANNEL MINING ACTIVITIES

In the late 1980s, eight mining companies operated in the active channel (Fig. 2). Two additional sites had also been proposed upstream of those already in production. All sites were situated according to property ownership boundaries, and mining activities were designed to maximize aggregate production. Channel morphology, sediment transport characteristics, or potentially significant habitat localities were not prevailing issues.

The San Luis River, which 20 yr ago was an ephemeral wash with a wide, frequently inundated floodplain, has been extensively modified. Along the length of the river, the bed alternated between unmined channel and mined pits. Mining excavations intercepted the aquifer along the low flow channel, creating discontinuous lakes. In addition, portions of the low flow channel, were channelized in a loosely coordinated flood control effort, and areas in the floodplain were encroached upon and developed. The modifications of the San Luis Rey River are apparent when archival aerial photographs are compared to more recent photos. Mining and flood control projects stretch from the river mouth to Pala, as shown in Figure 2.

The mining excavations and channelized river sections ranged from 3.7 to 7.6 m (12 to 25 ft) in depth, relative to adjacent unmined riverbed elevations. One large excavation was 21 m (70 ft) deeper than the adjacent riverbed. Another major alteration in the river bed occurred in the City of Oceanside where an 11.6-km (7.2-mi) reach of channel was graded and levees constructed for a U.S. Army Corps of Engineers flood control project. The project was recently constructed to protect urban development in the floodplain. Channelization through levee construction precludes flooding portions of the natural floodplain. Floodwater that would normally spread into the floodplain is contained within the modified channel. The increase in water volume in the channel may increase flow velocities; such increased velocities may, in turn, accelerate streambed degradation or stream bank erosion.

MINING EXCAVATIONS AND SEDIMENT TRANSPORT

Despite the proliferation of mining activities on the San Luis Rey River, extraction volumes are rarely documented for the public record. This is partly because production data is considered proprietary and partly because of a lack of coordinated oversight. Conditions stated in stream mining use permits typically provide an order-of-magnitude estimate of annual extraction rates but generally underestimate cumulative removal volumes because of undocumented operations and overproduction at specific sites.

Large and deep mining excavations are efficient sediment traps. Deep mining pits within active portions of the channel tend to slow water velocities and trap material in transport. The pit floor ultimately acts as a new, lower base level for the channel. Consequently, the upstream river bed will increase in slope to adjust to the new, lower base level. From a hydraulic perspective, the downstream excavation has the effect of lowering the watersurface profile to induce a higher velocity in the adjacent upstream channel. The higher velocity, with its greater sediment transport capability, will remove sediment from the upstream channel boundary and result in scour—also called headcutting. Some of the scoured material will then be deposited in the excavation site where the velocity slows down (Chang, 1993).

In the San Luis Rey River, deep pit mines acted as sediment transport sinks and resulted in downstream flow with a high

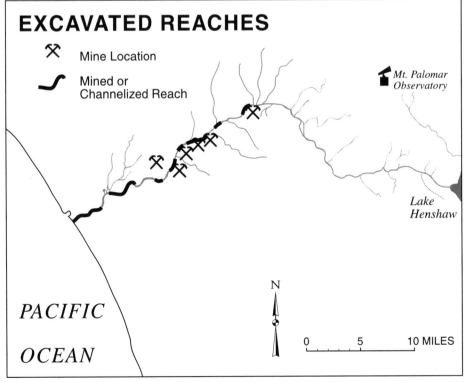

Figure 2. Excavated and channelized river reaches are extensive along the lower San Luis Rey River.

capacity for sediment transport, which eroded the downstream pit boundary. Several sites may become linked together by this process of scour of the downstream pit boundary and headcutting of the upstream pit boundary (Fig. 3). The process of scour, headcutting, and refill continues until the stream reaches a state of equilibrium, eventually refilling the pits at a lower profile grade.

Alternatively, excavations that mimic the natural channel grade tend to be least disruptive to the sediment transport continuum. Minimizing the gradient into and out of the excavation reduces potential headcutting and downstream scour processes. Depending on the excavated shape of the channel, the condition may be conducive either to sediment transport or, alternatively, sediment deposition.

SEDIMENT TRANSPORT MODELS

Numerical sediment transport models utilize fluid and sediment continuity and momentum principles along with empirical equations that predict river behavior. If accurate, these models would predict river behavior including aggradation and degradation trends and lateral channel erosion, given different mining scenarios. Unfortunately, the state of the art is not yet sufficient to produce definitive answers (Dawdy and Vanoni, 1986). In 1983 the National Research Council studied six of the available sediment transport models in order to determine the effect of riverbed degradation during flood passage on flood stage. They concluded that "the available input data on channel geometry, bed material characteristics, etc., generally are inadequate to permit full utilization of the capabilities of erodible-bed models" (Committee on Hydrodynamic Computer Methods for Flood Insurance Studies, 1983). For example, two numerical models (FLUVIAL-12 and HEC-6) were used to predict the behavior of the San Luis Rey River. The HEC-6 study concluded "the average degradation of Reach 2 [old

Route 395] was calculated to be 0.2 ft during the 100-yr flood event" (Simons, Li and Associates, Inc., 1992). The FLUVIAL-12 study differed significantly, predicting 4.6 m (15 ft) of channel degradation at the old Route 395 structure (Chang, 1993).

As noted above, numerical sediment transport models have their limitations since they should be calibrated to the individual river. This involves taking physical measurements of the riverbed before, during, and after a flood, simulating the same magnitude and duration event with the numerical model, and comparing the two data sets. Where a close match is not accomplished, the model parameters need to be adjusted. It is also important to note that prediction of the intensity of the next flood event is stochastic. The actual flood magnitude and intensity are only as good as the hydrologist's statistical analysis. Aggregate demand, conversely, may be constant or may increase as the population grows. Sediment replenishment will need to await the next significant flood event, which may or may not occur within a given time period following extraction. In the case of the San Luis Rey River, small-scale mining was sustained over a long time period as pits were replenished without significant impacts. During the 1980s, however, intensive mining to supply urban buildout occurred with little sediment replenishment, as a result of a prolonged drought. This condition resulted in a series of deep, unstable pits.

Longitudinal profiles of the San Luis River were surveyed in 1973, 1986, 1988, 1990, 1991, 1992, and 1993 and cover the mined portions of channel (Fig. 4). Some portions of the channel were also surveyed in 1994. The longitudinal profiles show the low flow channel thalweg, including mining pits, where present. These surveys illustrate a general lowering trend in the river between 1973 and 1994. Average degradation (1973 to 1992) was on the order of 3.1 m (10 ft) (Parsons, Brinckerhoff, Gore and Storrie, Inc., 1993). The profiles graphically show that pit boundary erosion and refilling in the deepest portions of several of the excavations occurred during the 1993 floods (Fig. 5). Many of

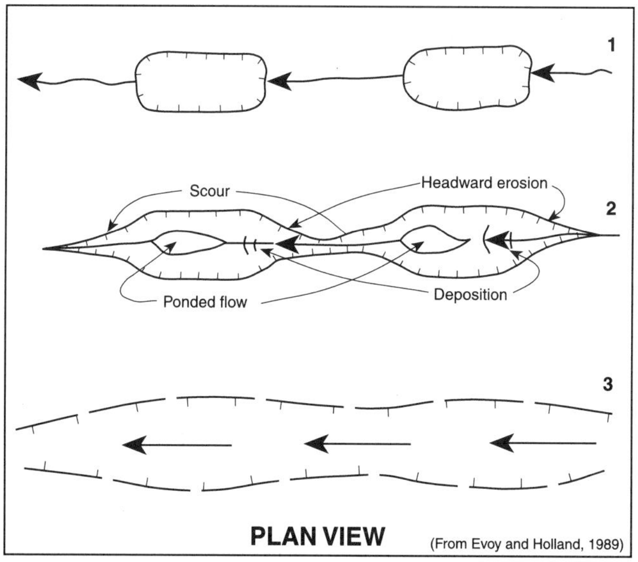

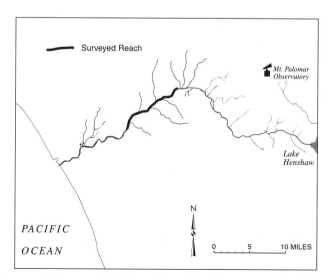

Figure 3. Headward erosion and downstream scour modify excavation boundaries during flood flows.

Figure 4. Surveys of limited portions of the San Luis Rey River were completed in 1973, 1986, 1988, 1990, 1991, 1992, and 1993.

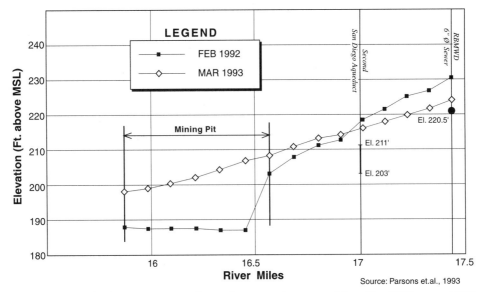

Figure 5. Erosional adjustments are prominent when comparing sequential profiles (1992 versus 1993) of this deep mining excavation.

these 1993 erosional adjustments represent the extraction of material in excess of the actual replenishment.

Numerical modeling has been used to simulate the statistical occurrence of flood events for a 100-yr period on the San Luis Rey River (Parsons, Brinckerhoff, Gore and Storrie, Inc., 1993). The analysis indicates that, without additional mining, 1.5 to 3.1 m (5 to 10 ft) of material would deposit in the channel within a 100-yr period. This is an amount commensurate to the degradation that has occurred during the last 20 yr, as shown in the longitudinal surveys. This suggests 5 to 10 times the actual volume of sediment delivered to the reach was mined.

IMPACTS TO INFRASTRUCTURE

Infrastructure that may be affected by channel degradation on the San Luis Rey and its tributaries includes bridges, aqueducts, sewer lines, and natural gas conduits (Fig. 6). Most bridges crossing the San Luis Rey River are supported by piers within the active channel. Aqueducts and gas lines are buried within the channel bed. Other utilities are suspended from the bridge decks and depend on the integrity of the bridges for their support. The tolerance of the crossings to channel changes varies with the design. Generally, the crossings are designed to withstand local channel changes (local scour and fill) that occur during a flood. A progressive and persistent lowering of the channel bed over several kilometers, however, added to the destabilization or failure of several structures during the January 1993 floods. For example, during the 1993 storms, the riverbed beneath the old Route 395 structure lowered 2.4 to 3.1 m (8 to 10 ft) (Fig. 7). The channel degradation increased pile exposure beyond its design capacity, necessitating closure and subsequent replacement of the structure (Fig. 8). The replacement construction cost is estimated to be $4.5 million.

Lowering of the elevation of the San Luis Rey River initi-

ated erosion that headcut up Horseranch Creek, a tributary to the San Luis Rey River. This headcutting contributed to the failure of the Route 76 bridge over Horseranch Creek—the only state bridge failure during the 1993 floods (Fig. 9). Although no cross section information is available, this structure had previously withstood larger flood events without problems; thus it is assumed that local scour alone did not cause the bridge failure.

Flood waters washed out additional infrastructure including the Couser Canyon Road (which housed a U.S. Geological Survey gauging station) and West Lilac Road bridges. The demise of these crossings was likely a combination of inadequate capacity to pass the discharges and riverbed degradation. The storms also exposed

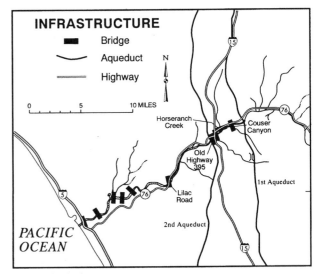

Figure 6. Extensive infrastructure, including bridges, aqueducts, and utilities, has been impacted by changes in bed elevations in the San Luis Rey River.

Channel Section for Old Highway 395

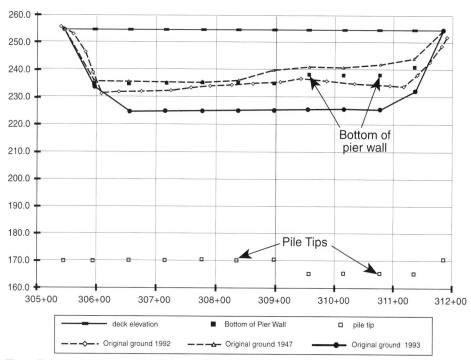

Figure 7. Degradation at the Old Highway 395 bridge has been progressive, as noted in periodic bridge cross section surveys. Additional degradation during the 1993 floods exposed the pile-supported footings, necessitating closure and replacement.

the San Diego Gas and Electric Company's (SDG&E) gas line (located near the Couser Canyon Road), which was replaced approximately 4.6 m (15 ft) deeper than the damaged crossing.

Two aqueduct crossings bring imported water to San Diego County (Fig. 6). Each consists of multiple high-pressure pipelines set into the channel alluvium (Fig. 10). The progressive loss of cover material was a major concern for the San Diego County Water Authority. In March 1991, local scour exposed the pipeline at the downstream crossing. The crossing was retrofitted with a sheet pile drop structure and armored on both sides with riprap. Grade stabilizers set a minimum bed elevation for the upstream channel, acting as a local base level. Sediment transported by flow in the channel is interrupted by the grade stabilizer. Bed material is deposited upstream of the stabilizer until the bed elevation exceeds the height of the top of the stabilizer; at that time downstream transport resumes. During the January 1993 floods, flows outflanked the downstream aqueduct crossing where the south abutment was inadequately keyed into the streambank. San Diego County Water Authority embedded an additional 61 m (200 ft) of sheet piling into the south bank to avoid future avulsion.

AGENCIES WITH JURISDICTION

In California, surface mining activities are regulated under the state Surface Mining and Reclamation Act of 1975 (SMARA). The state legislature has amended SMARA a dozen times since 1975

in order to improve SMARA's effectiveness. Legislative changes to SMARA in 1990 required, among other things, annual reporting and financial assurances for reclamation of mined land and provided additional state oversight over mining activities.

SMARA requires a reclamation plan to be prepared for all surface mines in California. Reclamation plans offer a vehicle for mitigating mining impacts. The purpose of the plan is to "prevent

Figure 8. Photograph taken after the 1993 floods at the Old Highway 395 bridge shows the exposed piles of the structure. (Caltrans photograph.)

Figure 9. Failure of the Horseranch Creek bridge on Highway 76 is attributed to several factors, including bed lowering in the San Luis Rey River, which may have headcut up Horseranch Creek, a tributary to the San Luis Rey River. (Office of Mine Reclamation photograph.)

or minimize adverse effects" of mining and "reclaim mined land to a usable condition that is readily adaptable for alternative uses." Although SMARA mandates the above conditions, it provides little guidance to accomplish these goals. The preparation of a reclamation plan was a permit condition for mining applications on the San Luis Rey River. The approach usually taken in the reclamation plan for mining projects in the San Luis Rey River was that the landform created by mining the site would be revegetated. The reclamation plans treated the mines as though they were static landforms, unrelated to one another. They did not adequately

address the erosion potential at excavation boundaries, offsite erosional impacts, or cumulative impacts on sediment transport and riparian communities—nor did they provide timetables to initiate reclamation activities.

San Diego County is the primary local SMARA lead agency for mining activities on the San Luis Rey River. In 1990, a San Luis Rey "river sweep" was conducted by San Diego County in response to public involvement and agency concerns. A number of impediments to effective regulation became apparent at that time. Generally there was no mechanism to verify adherence to an approved reclamation plan. Excavations usually formed deep groundwater ponds, the depth of which was problematic. Excavated sand and gravel that exceeded permit limits simply could not be replaced. Five of the eight operations were found to be out of compliance with their reclamation plans or permit conditions and subsequently shut down.

In 1989, the Federal Environmental Protection Agency (EPA) stepped up Clean Water Act programs in the San Luis Rey basin. San Luis Rey mining operators were notified that they were to obtain a permit from the U.S. Army Corps of Engineers to authorize the placement of fill within "waters of the United States," which was needed for mining operations. The EPA was concerned with cumulative impacts of mining on sediment transport and riparian communities. The three sites remaining in operation after the county "sweep" were cited by the EPA for Clean Water Act violations in 1992.

The EPA provided assistance to the county in obtaining federal funding to prepare portions of a comprehensive watershed and river corridor management plan. The EPA-funded studies focused on water quality and wetlands within the San Luis Rey

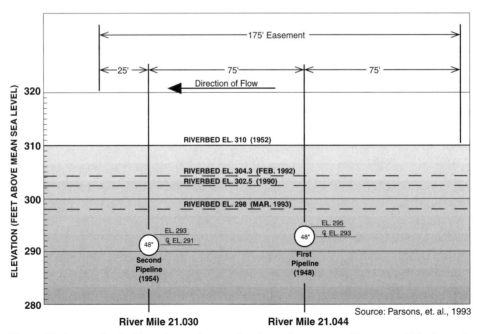

Figure 10. Progressive bed lowering at the aqueduct located upstream of Interstate 15 is shown in sequential cross sections.

basin. A portion of the funds was used to identify and classify significant remaining wetland habitat and degraded habitat that could be improved. A Resource Report (Lettieri, McIntyre and Associates, Inc. 1995) has been prepared that summarizes existing information that has been collected for the San Luis Rey watershed. At the time of this writing efforts continue toward securing funding to prepare the comprehensive plan.

MANAGEMENT RECOMMENDATIONS/ CONCLUSIONS

Two primary management approaches are used by local agencies to regulate mining operations in rivers: (1) extraction of the estimated watershed sediment yield and (2) redlining. The first, which allows the removal of an average annual influx of aggregate or a portion of that expected as replenishment, is currently used in managing the gravel mining in Humboldt County's Mad River (Crossett, 1993) and rivers in Lake County. The approach has been recommended for Mendocino County's Garcia River and Sonoma County's Russian River. Ideally, this management scheme first requires estimating watershed sediment yield and then equitably distributing that volume among the operators (somewhat like adjudicating a groundwater basin). Primary concerns include the level of confidence that can be given to the watershed sediment supply estimate and ways to allow downstream sediment transport by extracting less than the estimated replenished volume.

The second approach is to establish a redline elevation for critical reaches of the river, with a "critical" reach defined as one with both infrastructure and mining present or proposed. The intent is to establish a not-to-exceed elevation for excavations based on the design tolerances of the infrastructure. The redline should be designed to provide soil cover over bridge foundations, for example. Where infrastructure is present, this management approach requires modeling the river with a sediment transport model to design the redline elevation. Where biotic resources are present, the current bed elevation is often used as the red-line elevation under the assumption that the existing conditions are desirable for a healthy river ecology. The redline approach generally has been initiated to allow extraction in excess of watershed sediment yield for a limited period of time, until the redline is met. Thereafter mining matches the rate of aggradation above the redline gradient.

A redline has been implemented in Ventura County's Santa Clara River and Yolo County's Cache Creek (Woodward-Clyde Consultants, 1976). It should be noted that the channel thalweg is currently approximately 1.5 m (5 ft) below the redline elevation at the Route 101 bridge across the Santa Clara River. These redlines were very close to the streambed elevations at the time of design. The Sisquoc/Santa Maria River Specific Plan that is in preparation (Santa Barbara/San Luis Obispo Counties) also proposes a redline (Balance Hydrologics, Inc., 1992). This redline would be approximately 6.1 m (20 ft) lower than the existing riverbed, allowing a significant volume of material to be mined. Part of this proposal involves replacement of a local agency bridge (primar-ily financed by the Federal Highway Bridge Rehabilitation and Replacement Program) and grade stabilization structure construction on each tributary channel.

A redline has been proposed for the San Luis Rey River in connection with a study to design protection for the San Diego Water Authority's aqueducts (Parsons, Brinckerhoff, Gore and Storrie, Inc., 1993). The elevations for the redline correspond to the 1973 thalweg elevation, which is consistently higher than the 1993 bed elevations. The riverbed would theoretically require sufficient time and minimal excavation to aggrade to the 1973 elevations.

Monitoring needs to be part of any river mining management scheme (Sandecki, 1989). A data collection program is set up to measure and document trends in the physical shape of the channel and record extraction and replenishment volumes. The data analysis should include collection of repeated topographic surveys, inspection of sequential aerial photographs, and review of cumulative mine production records. The response of the channel, monitored by the topographic surveys, allows a rate of channel aggradation or degradation to be calculated. It verifies the replenishment estimate, checks the accuracy of the numerical model, and allows for natural variations in sediment supply. We believe this adaptive management technique is key to effective river management.

The monitoring effort can be relatively straightforward. Planning departments ensure compliance by comparing the design elevation to actual field surveys and checking air photos for mining boundaries, protected vegetation, and so on. The challenge arises when the riverbed elevation falls below the redline, or when there is minimal replenishment. It is often very difficult to change the redline elevation upward once established because it is perceived as taking marketable aggregate from an operation. In the case of inadequate replenishment, other sources need to be considered.

One of the most challenging management scenarios occurs when demand usually far exceeds in-channel supply. This occurs most frequently in urban areas. Other potential material sources such as off channel sites should be considered when the channel itself cannot supply the quantity of resources needed. Off channel excavation sites are generally located within the 100-yr floodplain because it corresponds to the location of the aggregate deposit. Potential questions include; (1) Is a land buffer adequate, or are structural measures (such as levees) needed to isolate the site from the river? (2) What effect will the excavation have on channel processes if intercepted? (3) What would be impacted? It is often possible to design the excavations to minimize environmental impacts and provide a beneficial reclaimed land use. One must consider that these features will be long lived; therefore structural methods will require maintenance in perpetuity.

The San Luis Rey River experienced rapid morphologic changes during the 1993 storms, which impacted infrastructure and wildlife. These morphologic changes can be linked to the over-extraction of gravel within the river system. Since minimal information was available, the decisionmakers were unable to determine the cause of the problem or mitigate existing or potential future impacts. San Diego County in cooperation with resource and responsible agencies appears to be headed in the right direction by funding necessary studies to evaluate potential impacts and develop plans to manage the river resources. Only by looking at the entire river system can the responsible agencies begin to balance the competing needs of the river between providing necessary aggregate resources for urbanization while protecting infrastructure and wildlife.

REFERENCES CITED

Balance Hydrologics, Inc., 1992, Hydrologic and geomorphic factors affecting management of the Lower Sisquoc River Alluvial Corridor, Santa Barbara, California: Santa Barbara, California, Prepared for Southern Pacific Milling Company, 72 p.

Bowers, J. C., 1993, Southern California storms and floods of January–February 1993: U.S. Geologic Survey Water Fact Sheet, Open File Report 93-411, 2 p.

California Division of Mines and Geology, 1983, Mineral land classification: Western San Diego County Special Report 153, 28 p.

Chang, H. H., 1993, Hydrologic/hydraulic study for proposed bridge at Old Highway 395 on the San Luis Rey River: San Diego, California, Prepared for San Diego Department of Public Works, 6 p.

Collins, B., and Dunne, T., 1990, Fluvial geomorphology and river-gravel mining: California Department of Conservation, Division of Mines and Geology Special Publication 98, 29 p.

Committee on Hydrodynamic Computer Methods for Flood Insurance Studies, 1983, An evaluation of flood-level prediction using alluvial-river models: Washington D.C., National Research Council, National Academy Press, 127 p.

Crossett, C. M., 1993, Overmining causes undermining (it's a mad mad river), *in* Proceedings, American Society of Civil Engineers, 1993 National Conference on Hydraulic Engineering: New York, American Society of Civil Engineers, p. 1877–1881.

Dawdy, D. R., and Vanoni, V. A., 1986, Modeling alluvial channels: Water Resources Research, v. 22, p. 71S–81S.

Evoy, B., and Holland, M., 1989, Surface and groundwater management in surface mined-land reclamation: California Department of Conservation, Division of Mines and Geology Special Report 163, 39 p.

Kondolf, G. M., 1993, Management of coarse sediment on regulated rivers: University of California, California Water Resources Center, Report 80, ISSN 0575-4968, 128 p.

Lettieri, McIntyre and Associates, Inc., 1995, San Luis Rey River resources report: San Diego, California, Prepared for the County of San Diego Department of Parks and Recreation, 229 p.

Parsons, Brinckerhoff, Gore and Storrie, Inc. 1993, Permanent protection of the San Luis Rey River aqueduct crossings, Preliminary Design Report Volume I: San Diego, California, Prepared for the San Diego County Water Authority, 166 p.

Sandecki, M., 1989, Aggregate mining in river systems: California Geology, v. 42, p. 88–94.

Simons, Li and Associates, Inc., 1992, Old Highway 395 bridge scour investigation and erosion control alternatives: San Diego, California, Prepared for San Diego Department of Public Works, 65 p.

Woodward-Clyde Consultants, 1976, Aggregate extraction management study, County of Yolo, California: Woodland, California, Prepared for the County of Yolo Planning Department, Aggregate Resources Management Committee, 128 p.

MANUSCRIPT ACCEPTED BY THE SOCIETY JANUARY 29, 1997

Geological Society of America
Reviews in Engineering Geology, Volume XI
1997

Impact of the 1992–1993 winter storms on hydroconsolidation, differential settlement, and ground fissures, Murrieta area, southwestern Riverside County, California

Roy J. Shlemon
P.O. Box 3066, Newport Beach, California 92659
Mack Hakakian
29489 Via Las Colinas, No. 227, Temecula, California 92592

ABSTRACT

The 1992–1993 winter storms in Murrieta, California, produced rainfall that exceeded 200% of normal. This water infiltrated into buried channels filled with up to 30 m of alluvium and thus added to rising water levels caused by accelerating urban runoff during the previous 5 yr. Downstream valleys in the California Oaks area of Murrieta, now modified to support golf courses, were little affected by the rainfall, for most of the underlying sediments had already been saturated. Upstream, however, narrow alluvium-filled valleys were subjected to 3 to 4 m of groundwater-level rise in a 2-month period. Depending on local channel geometry and presence of fill loads, the 1992–1993 storms accelerated alluvial saturation, hydroconsolidation of collapsible soils, differential settlement, and formation of ground fissures. This combined natural and man-induced rise in regional groundwater levels damaged many houses and streets and locally impaired underground utilities. Alleged damages exceed $50 million, and litigation continues unabated. The Murrieta (California Oaks) hydroconsolidation, differential settlement, and ground fissures provide a case study of new challenges to the engineering geologist in California.

INTRODUCTION

The exceptionally high rainfall during the 1992–1993 winter in southern California produced the almost expected results: floods, landslides and mudflows, levee and bridge failures, loss of life, and property damage in the order of hundreds of millions of dollars. But other, more subtle impacts also occurred. Specifically, regional groundwater levels at Murrieta in southwestern Riverside County rose rapidly, saturating Holocene alluvium in 30-m-deep old stream channels. Unfortunately, much of the alluvium had been left in place during grading in the previous few years and hence was "loaded" by compacted fill and by hundreds of new homes and related infrastructure. The result was accelerated hydroconsolidation of underlying alluvium, increasing distress to infra-

structure and houses, failure of a main arterial street, major damage to an elementary school, and exacerbation of ongoing litigation.

This chapter focuses on a particular section of Murrieta, namely, the California Oaks area, currently the site of a Special Geologic Report Zone set up to assess the cause of ground fissures and structural distress. We first provide a chronology of fissure occurrence in the Murrieta and adjacent Temecula areas. Second, we set forth the geomorphic and geologic setting, noting the conditions favorable to alluvial hydroconsolidation and related differential settlement in California Oaks. Third, we describe the form and causation of the Murrieta fissures. And finally, we assess the relative impact of the 1992–1993 winter precipitation on rising groundwater levels induced by increasing runoff of urban irrigation water.

Shlemon, R. J., and Hakakian, M., 1997, Impact of the 1992–1993 winter storms on hydroconsolidation, differential settlement, and ground fissures, Murrieta area, southwestern Riverside County, California, *in* Larson, R. A., and Slosson, J. E., eds., Storm-Induced Geologic Hazards: Case Histories from the 1992–1993 Winter in Southern California and Arizona: Boulder, Colorado, Geological Society of America Reviews in Engineering Geology, v. XI.

CHRONOLOGY OF TEMECULA-MURRIETA GROUND FISSURES

Murrieta and the adjacent City of Temecula were the locus of rapid, late 1980s urbanization that occurred in southwestern Riverside County. Population increased from a few thousand in 1980 to well over 100,000 by 1990, much of this increase taking place between 1985 and 1990. Most people in the area, formerly known as "Rancho California," are now residents of the new cities of Temecula and Murrieta, incorporated in 1990 and 1991, respectively.

The urbanization of both cities spread from the "Old Town" main streets within the approximately 3-km-wide Temecula-Murrieta Valley (Elsinore Trough) onto coalescing alluvial fans, floodplain and dissected topography underlain by the late Tertiary–Quaternary Pauba formation, particularly east of Interstate Highways 15 and 215 (Fig. 1). Massive grading was the norm during the 1980s, and often 1,000-house subdivisions were planned. Geotechnical issues were generally few: concern with setbacks from active traces of the Elsinore fault zone and assessment of potential seismically induced liquefaction.

Temecula fissures

In late 1987, the relatively rapid but geotechnically "peaceful" urbanization of the Temecula and Murrieta areas was interrupted by ground fissures and related structural damage that particularly affected new tracts in Wolf Valley, south of Temecula, and business parks north of the Old Town center (Fig. 1). Alleged damages exceeded $50 million (Corwin et. al., 1991). Spurred by litigation, numerous geotechnical investigations were carried out to determine the cause and extent of the so-called Temecula fissures. Hypotheses for fissure origin were many; of these, two were paramount: (1) The fissures were caused by aseismic creep along a previously unrecognized zone of faults, and (2) the fissures resulted from pumping groundwater within this portion of the Elsinore Trough, ostensibly engendered by several new, 350-m-deep production wells (Shlemon and Davis, 1992). Although perhaps still arguable, the fissures are now believed to result from pumping-induced tensile stresses localized along previously unrecognized active (Holocene) faults along the western margin of the Elsinore Trough—mainly the Wolf Valley fault on the south and the Murrieta Creek fault on the north (Fig. 1; Kennedy, 1977; Bergmann and Rockwell, 1989).

Murrieta fissures

In mid-1989, ground cracks were observed on and adjacent to Jackson Road in the California Oaks area of Murrieta (Fig. 2). A year later, new homes constructed on bluffs adjacent to golf

Figure 1. Location of Old Town in Temecula and Murrieta in the Elsinore Trough (the Murrieta-Temecula and Wolf Valley grabens), the 1987 Temecula fissures, and the 1989 to present Callifornia Oaks fissures in Murrieta (see Fig. 4 for enlargement).

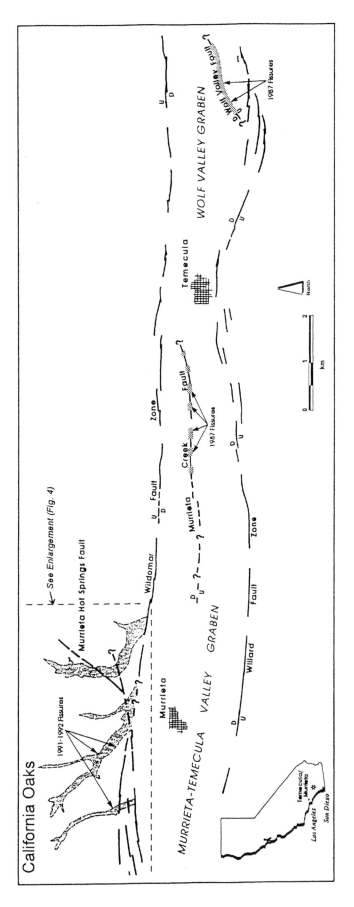

Figure 2. Typical ground fissures in building-site compacted fill, California Oaks area. The fissures coincide with the underlying alluvium-bedrock contact.

Figure 3. Ground fissure development and differential settlement affecting a typical posttensioned foundation, California Oaks area.

courses were affected; and by the end of that year, over 20 homeowners reported significant distress to their structures (Fig. 3). Additionally, in 1990, another 20, as yet unbuilt lots were impacted by ground fissures. The fissures were geomorphically similar to those in Temecula that coincided with faults and thus were thought to have been produced by groundwater pumping. However, no groundwater pumping was taking place in California Oaks; rather, almost all water for urban and recreational use, particularly golf courses, was imported. The origin of the fissures was unknown, and the stage thus was set for litigation and a plethora of associated geotechnical investigations (Shlemon, 1995).

Initial hypotheses as to the origin of the California Oaks fissures were mainly (1) control by unrecognized active faults, comparable to the nearby Temecula area, and (2) unanticipated primary settlement of compacted fill and compression of left-in-place alluvium. Owing to the increasing distress in many structures, particularly tilting, and to formation of ground fissures, the County of Riverside established a formal Special Geologic Study Zone for most of the California Oaks area and adjacent watershed (Fig. 4). The zone, implemented under the 16 May 1991 Resolution 91-285 (County of Riverside, 1991), essentially said that no additional building permits could be issued until adequate geotechnical investigations were conducted (compliance reports) and appropriate assurances were given to county building officials concerning the

safety and welfare of the residents and their property. The immediate impact of the zone was effectively a building-permit moratorium. This pleased neither the developers nor the residents trying to sell houses, for nobody knew the cause of the fissures and where such phenomena might occur in the near future.

Unfortunately, too, many newspaper articles, although perhaps well-meaning, were often sensational and bereft of factual data, further fanning the flames of misinformation and ultimately litigation. Additional complications occurred when the City of Murrieta was incorporated 2 months later on July 1, 1991. The city adopted the county-declared Special Geologic Study Zone as well as the compliance reports previously issued by the county based on technical documentation and certification provided by developers' geotechnical consultants. Within a month of incorporation, areas previously accepted as "appropriately mitigated" were found to be riddled with new fissures. In this case, clearly, the consultants' mitigation had failed, and the cause of the fissures was therefore something other than either active faults, which were not found, or unanticipated primary settlement of compacted fills and compression of underlying alluvium. Only after completing regional investigations, paid for by a consortium of developers, was it determined that the subsurface water levels, particularly within old stream channels, were rising rapidly (Pacific Soils Engineering, Inc., 1992). Although the late 1980s were a time of

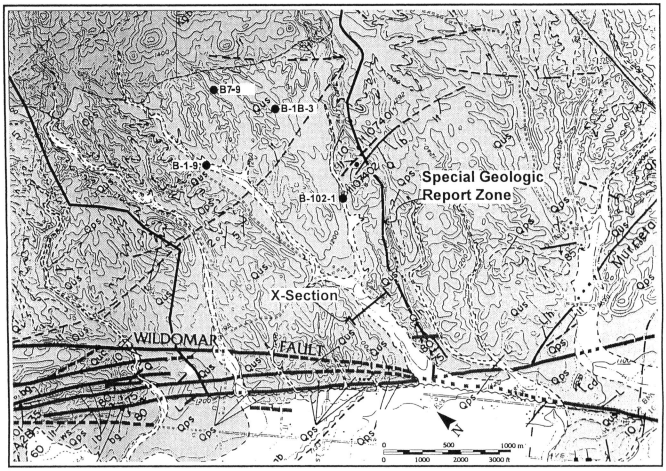

Figure 4. A portion of the California Oaks Special Geological Report Zone bordered by the Wildomar fault on the south and elsewhere delimited by drainage divides. Principal geologic units are the Quaternary Pauba Formation sandstone (Qps) and the "unnamed sandstone" (Qus) of Kennedy (1977). Schematic channel cross section shown in Figure 7; representative geotechnical data for upper-channel boring B7-9 given in Table 1 and illustrated in Figure 8. Hydrographs for representative upper and lower channel monitoring wells (B-1-9, B-1B-3, and B-102-1) discussed in text.

regional drought, this man-induced rise in water level, combined with left-in-place alluvium (collapsible soils) and compacted fill loads, proved conducive to accelerated hydroconsolidation and differential settlement (Shlemon and Hakakian, 1992). Most water apparently infiltrated the alluvium either from unlined channels within golf course areas or from upstream and sidestream urban irrigation (Figs. 5 and 6). This is still occurring, but was locally exacerbated by the winter storms of 1992–1993.

GEOMORPHIC AND GEOLOGIC SETTING

Geologically, the Murrieta fissure area, as delimited by the Riverside County Special Geologic Study Zone (Fig. 4), consists of moderately dissected terrain underlain by the Tertiary-Quaternary Pauba Formation ("bedrock") on the southwest, by Peninsular Range granitic rocks on the northeast, and by former incised channels now filled with up to 30 m of Holocene allu-

vium and sideslope-derived colluvium. The channels trend southwestward across the Wildomar fault and into the Elsinore Trough (Fig. 4). Prior to development, only episodic surface flow was present in the canyons, emanating mostly from storm-derived overland flow and locally from springs along the contact between granitic rocks and the Pauba Formation.

As shown schematically (Fig. 7), the California Oaks channels are asymmetric in profile and the bedrock-alluvium subsurface contact is locally steeper than about 2:1. The channel-filling alluvium is mostly fine silty sand to sandy silt, derived from adjacent bedrock. Alluvium thickness generally increases downstream, reaching about 35 m at the Wildomar fault. West of the fault, in the adjacent Temecula-Murrieta Valley (Fig. 1), probable Holocene sediments are much thicker, locally exceeding 300 m (Mann, 1955; Kennedy, 1977).

No obvious ground fissures or differential settlement has occurred west of the Wildomar fault. The fault was therefore selected to mark the southwestern boundary of the Special Geo-

Figure 5. A California Oaks golf course constructed within an alluvium-filled channel, showing unlined drainage that accelerates infiltration of adjacent urban runoff.

Figure 6. Structural distress in home built across the bedrock (Pauba Formation)-alluvium contact, golf course area, California Oaks.

logic Study Zone (Fig. 4; County of Riverside, 1991). The Wildomar is active according to State of California criteria (Hart, 1990), for it is demonstrably Holocene in age as indicated by several 1-km-long, en echelon 5- to 6-m-high escarpments and by historical seismicity (Mann, 1955; Kupferman and Shlemon, 1989). Movement is predominately right-lateral strike slip; the late Quaternary slip rate has been estimated as 5 to 6 mm/yr (Millman and Rockwell, 1986; Hull and Nicholson, 1992). Locally, the cumulative displacement is sufficient to block subsurface flow in the California Oaks channels. The Wildomar fault therefore acts as a leaky barrier and probably accounts for the upstream "damming" of water within the buried channels.

FORM AND CAUSATION OF THE MURRIETA FISSURES

Murrieta-area fissures typically are en echelon in pattern and often more than 20 m long. Their depth is unknown, but the fissures presumably extend to subsurface zones of saturation. The fissures are readily apparent on both paved areas and on graded, but as yet unbuilt, lots (Figs. 2 and 3). Mapping shows that the fissures almost perfectly coincide with bedrock-alluvium contacts, particularly where delimiting former ephemeral, and up to 300-m-wide, channels that now have been transformed into golf courses bordered by hundreds of overlooking "view" houses (Figs. 5 and 6).

When the Murrieta fissures were first observed in 1989, the cause was unknown. Multiple hypotheses were inferred, based on the presence of geomorphically similar features then having been investigated in the adjacent Temecula area (Corwin et. al., 1991; Shlemon and Davis, 1992; Shlemon and Hakakian, 1992). Additionally, similar ground fissures and oft-related subsidence were well documented in the literature, with their origin attributed to several causes, including groundwater withdrawal, hydroconsolidation of surface silty sediments, local shrink-swell characteristics, aseismic creep, and loss of support occasioned by hydrocarbon and salt mining. (See, for example, summaries in Holzer, 1984; Johnson, 1991; and Johnson et. al., 1990.)

The Murrieta fissures ultimately proved to have an origin generally unrecognized by the local geotechnical community, at least prior to site-specific investigations that began in 1990. It is now well documented that local hydroconsolidation and differential settlement in the Murrieta area are mainly caused by rising groundwater now saturating previously unwetted or only partially wetted alluvium (Pacific Soils Engineering, Inc., 1992). This phenomenon is common in arid and semiarid regions and has variously been described as soil collapse, hydrocompaction, hydroconsolidation, and wetting-induced collapse (Bara, 1976; Basma and Tuncer, 1992; Clemence and Finbarr, 1981; Curtin, 1973; Dudley, 1970; El-Ehwany and Houston, 1990; Gibbs and Bara, 1967). The wetting essentially destroys capillary bonds within the alluvium, thus resulting in sudden decrease in soil volume (hydroconsolidation). The rapid rise of groundwater in the California Oaks zone differs from the well-documented surface consolidation of loessial and other silty sediments usually produced by descending wetting fronts that emanate from the introduction of surface water onto previously unsaturated deposits (Bara, 1976; Beckwith and Hansen, 1989; Houston et. al., 1988; Lawton et. al., 1992; Panel on Land Subsidence, 1991; Poland et. al., 1975; Slaff, 1990). In this chapter we term the Murrieta-area rising groundwater and soil-collapse process as "hydroconsolidation"; however, the very descriptive designation "hydrocollapse" has also been used (Pacific Soils Engineering, Inc., 1992; Shlemon, 1995).

Driven by ongoing litigation and by the imposition of the Special Geologic Study Zone, a regional geotechnical investigation identified four principal factors necessary to produce the fis-

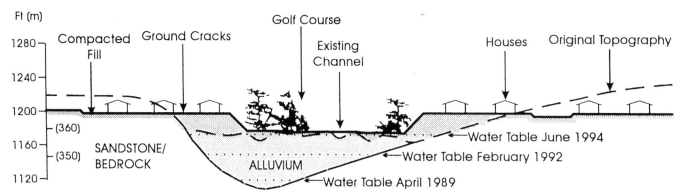

Figure 7. Schematic cross section across golf course channel showing 15-m water-table elevation rise between 1989 and 1994, the asymmetry of the subsurface alluvium-becrock contact, the typical site of ground cracks (fissures), and location of houses subject to hydroconsolidation-induced distress (see also Fig. 2).

sures and subsidence at Murrieta (Pacific Soils Engineering, Inc., 1992): (1) the presence of sediments susceptible to hydroconsolidation, (2) rising groundwater levels, (3) the presence of an overlying fill load, and (4) a relatively steep, usually greater than about 2:1, subsurface slope-contact between bedrock (granitic rock or Pauba Formation) and channel alluvium. All four of the above-specified conditions must be met before surface fissures are obvious.

Unfortunately, most potentially collapsible alluvium was left in place during initial grading of the California Oaks area, and removals were mainly limited to the upper few meters where obvious organic sediments were present or where dictated by design of the golf course. The hydroconsolidation susceptibility is indicated by geotechnical data for a representative boring (B7-9) emplaced in the upper reach of a California Oaks buried channel (Fig. 4; Table 1). Here, approximately 10 m of compacted fill overlies a grossly fining-upward, 14-m-thick section of silty sands that are particularly susceptible to collapse upon wetting (Pacific Soils Engineering, Inc., 1992). This susceptibility is indicated by the relatively low blow counts, moisture, and density and saturation values (Table 1). Four samples taken at 11 m, 11.5 m, 12.2 m, and 13.7 m, upon laboratory wetting collapsed between 0.49 and 1.3% (Fig. 8). Geotechnical data from more than about 50 other borings in the zone indicate that hydroconsolidation values of 1 to 3% are common (Pacific Soils Engineering, Inc., 1992). However, up to 10% soil collapse may occur in 2- to 3-m-thick sections of silt and fine sand, particularly in lower reaches of buried channels near the Wildomar fault (unpublished proprietary data).

The second condition conducive to differential settlement and fissures in the Murrieta area is saturation of left-in-place alluvium caused by a combination of rising subsurface water and infiltrating surface water. As shown on Figure 7, there was an approximately 20-m rise in channel groundwater levels between April 1989 and February 1992. This was a time of regional drought, and most water therefore probably entered the buried channels as urban runoff and from the unlined drainage channels

within the irrigated golf courses. Indeed, the rate of golf course irrigation is an estimated 1,250 mm/yr, more than three times the average annual precipitation in the Murrieta area. Since early 1992 urbanization has continued but at a lower rate, ostensibly owing to generally unfavorable economic conditions in the region. Nevertheless, water levels have continued to rise, and by June 1994 permanent surface flow was apparent in the golf course channels (Fig. 7). Approximately 10 monitoring wells are present in the lower fissure area; these show an average water-level rise of about 500 mm/month (J. Hanson, 1994, personal communication). Additionally, urban irrigation, primarily for landscaping in this semiarid region, is producing a descending wetting front that is now passing through compacted fill and into the upper section of left-in-place channel alluvium. This second wetting front, although lesser in impact than the rapid subsurface rise in water levels, likewise contributes to saturation of alluvium and hence to differential settlement (J. Hanson, 1994, personal communication).

The third condition required for Murrieta-area fissures is the presence of a fill load. Observation shows that fissures have not formed in natural terrain, even where groundwater levels have risen several meters. Most residential structures in the area are sited on fill caps ranging in thickness from a few to about 10 m. No quantifiable data are yet available to determine the relation of fill thickness to rapidity of fissure formation or to the amount of differential settlement. However, because approximately 70% of the 10,000 lots within the California Oaks Specific Plan area are as yet unbuilt and because many of these are on or adjacent to alluvium-filled channels, it is anticipated that additional hydroconsolidation, differential settlement, and fissure occurrence will take place in the likely event of continued groundwater rise.

The fourth principal factor controlling formation and location of the Murrieta fissures is steep subsurface slope, particularly the contact between the Pauba Formation or granitic bedrock and the adjacent channel margin. Fill caps and structures overlying these transition zones are particularly susceptible to fissures where the slope of the contact is generally about 2:1 or steeper. As shown in

**TABLE 1. GEOTECHNICAL DATA FOR REPRESENTATIVE BORING B7–9
SHOWING DEPTH AND PERCENT HYDROCONSOLIDATION OF FOUR SAMPLES
OF CALIFORNIA OAKS, UPPER-CHANNEL ALLUVIUM***

Depth (ft)	Blows (ft)	Moisture (%)	Density (pcf)	Saturation (%)	Consolidation (%)	
15.0	51	7.7	125	62		ARTIFICAL FILL – silty sand, moist dense
20.0	49	9.9	124	77		Gravelly silty sand, moist dense
25.0	23	12.9	123	97		Gravelly silty sand, very moist, medium dense
27.5	37	9.1	122	67		Gravelly silty sand, moist dense
30.0	75/10"	6.6	131	67		Gravelly silty sand, moist, dense
32.5	16	3.8	122	27		ALLUVIUM – silty sand and gravelly silty sand, moist, medium dense
35.0	15	4.6	117	29	1.19	Silty sand and gravelly silty sand, moist, medium dense
37.5	19	7.0	117	44	0.76	Silty sand, fine grained, moist medium dense
40.0	24	2.9	111	16	1.30	Silty sand, fine grained, moist medium dense
42.5	21	9.2	117	58		Silty sand, fine grained, moist medium dense
45.0	19	12.6	109	64	0.49	Silty sand, moist, firm
47.5	19	21.5	107	100		Silty sand, fine grained, moist, medium dense, with silt lenses
50.0	13	17.7	110	91		Silty sand, fine grained, wet, loose to medium dense
52.5	41	10.4	131	97	♦	Gravelly, clean, coarse-grained sand, wet, medium dense
55.0	37	14.5	123	100		Gravelly, silty sand, wet, medium dense
60.0	21	13.8	123	97		Interlayered fine silty sand, coarse-grained, gravelly sand, wet, medium dense
65.0	23	21.2	109	98		Gravelly, fine-grained silty sand, wet, medium dense
70.0	65	10.8	134	99		Gravelly sand, clean, coarse-grained, wet dense
75.0	53/10"	12.3	127	97		BEDROCK – SANDSTONE – fine to medium-grained, moist, hard
80.0	52/6"					

*See Figure 4 for location and Figure 8 for graphic depiction; data from Pacific Soils Engineering, Inc., 1992; 1 ft = 0.31 m.
♦ = water level June 1992.

the schematic cross section (Fig. 7), the outside, steeper channel margins provide the necessary setting for ground fissures. In contrast, the opposite, less steep contacts produce few, if any, obvious surface expressions of hydroconsolidation, despite the presence of susceptible alluvium, rising water levels, and a capping fill load.

THE 1992–1993 STORMS

Precipitation and flooding

A lengthy series of cyclonic storms affected much of southern California during the 1992–1993 rainy season, breaking a several-year-long drought. Most rain fell between 6 January and 28 February 1993, a period coincident with El Niño conditions in the tropical South Pacific. This situation resulted in total annual precipitation that typically exceeded 200% of normal (Bowers, 1993). About 940 mm of precipitation, some 223% of normal, was recorded at Temecula, the long-term recording station nearest to the California Oaks area. Approximately 82% of this rainfall (770 mm) occurred in January and February (County of Riverside Flood Control District, 1994).

The rain also produced severe flooding, particularly along Murrieta Creek (Fig. 1), where peak flows on January 16, 1993, were the highest of a 68-yr record. These flows overtopped a local streamflow gauging station and exceeded the previous high of February 21, 1980, by about 2 m (Bowers, 1993). Further, the resulting floods were more than a meter above the local 100-yr floodplain elevation, causing extensive property damage along Murrieta Creek (Peairs and Williams, 1994).

Regional rise in groundwater levels

The 1992–1993 storms also produced rapid rises in groundwater levels, particularly as recorded in California Oaks by scores of monitoring wells previously installed to assess the probable location and magnitude of hydroconsolidation-induced ground fissures (Pacific Soils Engineering, Inc. 1992).

The timing and rate of water-level rise varied throughout the area, as shown by hydrographs of monitoring wells. Unfortunately, at this writing most well data are still proprietary, owing to ongoing litigation, but three representative hydrographs provide a comparison of pre- and poststorm impact on regional water levels: monitoring well B-102-1, located in a major downstream golf course valley, and wells B-1B-3 and B-1-9, sited in upstream tributaries (Fig. 4).

Prior to the 1992–1993 rain, most downstream sediments had already been saturated owing to landscape and recreational runoff; hence storms produced relatively small rises in water levels. In contrast, sediments in the more narrow upstream valleys had been only partially saturated, and thus storm impact proved to be much greater. For example, water levels in the narrow valleys commonly rose 100% more rapidly during January and February 1993 than during the previous 12 to 18 months. This resulted in local "sudden" hydroconsolidation, initiation of new or extension of old ground fissures, increased differential settlement and, in one area, the tilting of an entire street (Figs. 9 and 10).

Monitoring Well B-102-1, in a typical lower golf course channel area (Fig. 4), recorded the prestorm rate and amount of

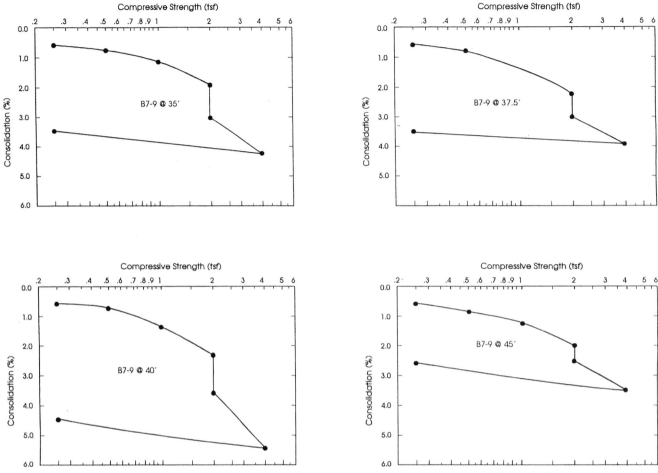

Figure 8. Soil collapse upon laboratory loading and wetting expressed as percent consolidation for four samples from representative upper-channel boring B7-9 (Fig. 4; Table 1; 1 ft = 0.31 m; 1 tsf = 1 kg/cm²).

groundwater-level rise. Here, water levels rose about 5 m during the 19 months preceding the January 1993 precipitation (Fig. 11). This prestorm rise mainly resulted from the dramatic increase in upstream urbanization since about 1987 and from the associated importation of water to new houses flanking the golf courses. The January 1993 precipitation, although 200% above normal, produced only a measured 300-mm rise in water level. This rise occurred within alluvium that was previously almost fully saturated and thus produced few additional ground fissures and little structural distress.

In contrast, upstream monitoring well B-1B-3 recorded a groundwater rise of only about 2 m during the 12 months preceding the January 1993 storms (Fig. 11). However, during January and February, an additional 4-m rise took place, far exceeding the previous 2-yr, man-induced rise. This rapid rise caused saturation of either previously unwetted or partially wetted alluvium, formation and extension of ground fissures, and a substantial increase in structural distress. Since March 1993, water levels have continued to rise owing to upstream and adjacent urban runoff and infiltration, but at a rate far lower than that associated with the January storms.

The upstream water level rise is also mirrored by the hydrograph for monitoring well B-1-9, similarly located in an upstream tributary (Fig. 11). This hydrograph recorded less than a 3-m rise in water level during the 13 months preceding the January 1993 storms. However, water levels rose another 3 m between January and March. This rapid rise was also accompanied by increased alluvial hydroconsolidation, by initiation of new fissures and rejuvenation of older ones, by failure of local infrastructure such as high-pressure water mains, and, downstream, by major distress to—and eventual abandonment of—a public school. Comparable to those of most other upstream tributaries, the monitoring well B-1-9 hydrograph shows that the 1992–1993 storms were followed by a continuing increase in water-level elevations but at a lessening rate, more consistent with the prestorm, man-induced rise.

SUMMARY AND CONCLUSIONS

The 1992–1993 storms at Murrieta had a major impact on fissure production and differential settlement. Yet, based on all evidence currently available, it is not likely that such damage would have occurred under wholly natural conditions; that is, prior to large-scale urbanization of the California Oaks area.

Figure 9. The closure of Jackson Road, a main California Oaks arterial, caused by hydroconsolidation-induced differential settlement associated with rapid water level rise during the winter of 1992–1993.

Figure 10. Hydroconsolidation and differential settlement in California Oaks manifested by 6 cm of horizontal compression and tilting of street and houses toward an alluvium-filled channel (to right of area in photograph). The curbing, here acting as a temporary "rigid beam," eventually failed. The houses remain unoccupied.

Although the 1992–1993 precipitation was relatively high, undoubtedly higher precipitation periodically occurred throughout the Holocene when sediments filled the California Oaks channels, tributaries to Murrieta Creek and the Elsinore Trough. Why then did alluvial hydroconsolidation, differential settlement, and ground fissures locally increase during the 1992–1993 winter rains, but not everywhere? This answer is seemingly best provided by the lower channel hydrographs, which show only minimal increase in water levels. Here, landscape water, totally imported into the area, had already percolated into the alluvial channels, perhaps aided by the presence of unlined channels in the golf courses. Prior to the storms, water levels had locally risen more than 30 m. The 1992–1993 precipitation was merely superimposed on an already regionally extensive rise in groundwater. Surface flow is now occurring in the golf course channels. Essentially, the near-surface flow regime in the California Oaks channels has entirely changed within the past several years. Potentially collapsible sediments that were never completely wetted for perhaps the past several thousand years are now fully saturated. This combination of collapsible sediments, rising water levels, structural fill load, and locally steep subsurface bedrock-alluvium contacts has set the stage for ground fissures, differential settlement,

and structural distress at a scale and rate heretofore unlikely to have occurred under natural conditions.

The impact of the 1992–1993 precipitation on regional water levels was not uniform; the downstream valleys, already almost completely saturated, were little affected. In contrast, the upstream, more narrow tributaries were greatly affected, especially where water levels rose more than 4 m in a 2-month period, causing particularly apparent damage to houses and infrastructure. Since the 1992–1993 storms, regional groundwater levels in the California Oaks area have continued to rise. The water is almost all derived from urban runoff. The rates of rise are controlled by local subsurface topography and by upstream urbanization. Hydroconsolidation, differential settlement, and ground fissures thus also continue, albeit now at a lower rate. Unfortunately, arguments still continue about whether these phenomena are part of a recognizable, predictable, and preventable sequence of events. Regardless, damage has been done, alleged to exceed about $50 million. Accordingly, litigation abounds, a sad learning experience to homeowners, developers, and geotechnical firms.

In retrospect, it appears that geotechnical problems in the California Oaks area of Murrieta are not unique. Rather, similar geologic and topographic conditions occur throughout Riverside County and undoubtedly elsewhere in the western United States. With increasing urbanization and the associated importation of irrigation water to such arid and semiarid areas, the potential for additional hydroconsolidation, differential settlement, and ground fissures is high. The geotechnical problems in Murrieta are merely an example of how combined natural and man-induced rises in groundwater levels present another challenge to the engineering geology community.

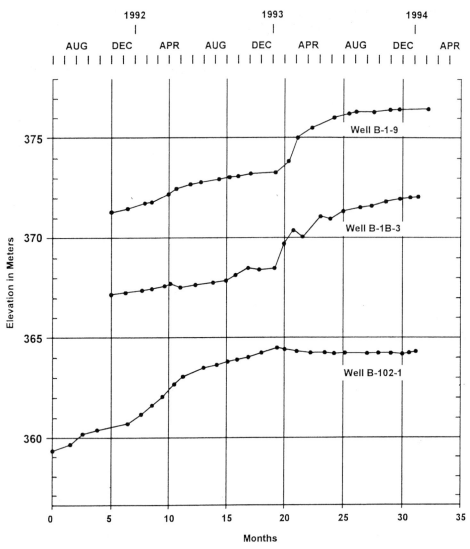

Figure 11. Hydrographs of representative upper channel (B-1-9; B-1B-3) and lower channel (B-102-1) monitoring wells, illustrating differential response to the 1992–1993 storms (see Fig. 4 for well location.)

ACKNOWLEDGMENTS

We thank the many geologists in the Temecula-Murrieta area, with whom we have had the pleasure of working these past several years, for sharing their knowledge about local differential settlement and fissure causation. We particularly acknowledge W. Williams, Riverside County Flood Control District, for making available precipitation data; and J. Hanson and his colleagues at Pacific Soils Engineering for providing unpublished hydrographic and geotechnical data; T. Holzer, J. Keaton, S. Slaff, J. Slosson, and D. Yoakum for their much-appreciated and thought-provoking reviews of a draft manuscript.

REFERENCES CITED

Bara, J. T., 1976, Collapsible soils: Philadelphia, America Society of Civil Engineers, National Convention preprint paper 2797, 13 p.

Basma, A. A., and Tuncer, E. R., 1992, Evaluation and control of collapsible soils: American Society of Civil Engineers, Journal of Geotechnical Engineering, v. 118, no. 10 (paper no. 48), p. 1491–1504.

Beckwith, G. H., and Hansen, L. A., 1989, Identification and characterization of collapsing alluvial soils of the western United States: *in* Kulhawy, F. H., ed., Foundation engineering—current principles and practices Volume 1: New York, American Society of Civil Engineers, v. 1, p. 143–160.

Bergmann, M., and Rockwell, T., 1989, The Murrieta Creek fault, a new branch of the Elsinore fault, Rancho California, Riverside County, California [abs.]: Geological Society of America Abstracts with Programs, v. 21, p. 5.

Bowers, J. C., 1993, Southern California floods and storms of January 1993: U.S. Geological Survey Open-file Report 93-411, Water Fact Sheet, 2 p.

Clemence, S. P., and Finnbarr, A. O., 1981, Design consideration for collapsible soils: American Society of Civil Engineers, Journal of the Geotechnical Engineering Division, v. 107, no. GT3, p. 305–317.

Corwin, E., Alhadeff, S., Oggle, S., and Shlemon, R., 1991, Earth fissures, urbanization and litigation: A case study from the Temecula area, southwestern Riverside County, California, *in* Johnson, L., ed.: Proceedings, International Symposium on Land Subsidence, Fourth, Houston, Texas: International

Association of Hydrological Sciences, Publication 200, p. 291–299.

County of Riverside, 1991, Special Geologic Report Zone, Resolution 91-125: Riverside, California, Department of Building and Safety, 4 p., maps.

County of Riverside Flood Control and Water Conservation District, 1994, Daily precipitation for 1992–1993 season, Temecula Station 88/3W-12P01; Index No. 217, unpaginated computer records.

Curtin, G., 1973, Collapsing soil and subsidence, *in* Moran, E. E., Slosson, J. E., Stone, R. O., and Yelverton, C. A., eds., Geology, seismicity, and environmental impact: Association of Engineering Geologists Special Publication, p. 89–101.

Dudley, J. G., 1970, Review of collapsing soils: American Society of Civil Engineers, Journal of the Soil Mechanics and Foundations Division, v. 96, no. SM3, p. 925-947.

El-Ehwany, M., and Houston, S. L., 1990, Settlement and moisture movement in collapsible soils: American Society of Civil Engineers, Journal of Geotechnical Engineering, v. 116, no. 10 (paper no. 25124), p. 1521–1535.

Gibbs, H. J., and Bara, J. P., 1967, Stability problems of collapsing soil: American Society of Civil Engineers, Journal of the Soil Mechanics and Foundations Division, v. 93, no. SM4, p. 577–594.

Hart, E. W., 1990, Fault-rupture zones in California: California Division of Mines and Geology Special Publication 42, 26 p.

Holzer, T. L., 1984, Ground failure induced by ground-water withdrawal from unconsolidated sediments, *in* Holzer, T. L., ed., Man-induced land subsidence: Geological Society of America Reviews in Engineering Geology, v. 6, p. 67–105.

Houston, S. L., Houston, W. N., and Spadola, D. J., 1988, Prediction of field collapse of soils due to wetting: American Society of Civil Engineers, Journal of Geotechnical Engineering, v. 114, no. 1 (paper no. 22107), p. 40–58.

Hull, G. and Nicholson, C., 1992, Seismotectonics of the northern Elsinore fault zone, southern California: Bulletin of the Seismological Society of America, v. 82, p. 800–818.

Johnson, A. I., ed., 1991, Land subsidence: Proceedings, International Symposium on Land Subsidence, Fourth, Houston, Texas: International Association of Hydrological Sciences, Publication 200, 690 p.

Johnson, A. I., Carognin, L., and Ubertini, L. eds., 1990, Land subsidence: Proceedings, International Symposium on Land Subsidence, Third, Venice, Italy: International Association of Hydrological Sciences, Publication 151, 939 p.

Kennedy, M. P., 1977, Recency and character of faulting along the Elsinore fault zone, southern Riverside County, California: California Division of Mines and Geology Special Report 131, 12 p., plate.

Kupferman, S., and Shlemon, R. J., 1989, Surface characteristics of the Wildomar fault: A geological hazard assessment, Rancho California area, southwestern Riverside County, California [abs.]: Association of Engineering Geology,

32nd Annual Meeting, Vail, Colorado, p. 87.

Lawton, E. C., Fragaszy, R. J., and Hetherington, M. D., 1992, Review of wetting-induced collapse in compacted soils: American Society of Civil Engineers, Journal of Geotechnical Engineering, v. 118, no. 9 (paper no. 2139), p. 1376–1394.

Mann, J. F., 1955, Geology of a portion of the Elsinore fault zone, California: California Division of Mines Special Report 43, 22 p.

Millman, D. E., and Rockwell, T. K., 1986, Neotectonics of the Elsinore fault in Temescal Valley, California, *in* Ehlig, P. L., ed., Neotectonics and faulting in southern California: Los Angeles, California, Geological Society of America Cordilleran Section Field Guidebook and Volume, p. 159–166.

Pacific Soils Engineering, Inc., 1992, Murrieta Special Geologic Report Zone—Report, Murrieta, California: Murrieta, California, Consultants' Technical Report for Builders Cooperative Association, 23 p., plates, appendices.

Panel on Land Subsidence, 1991, Mitigating losses from land subsidence in the United States: Washington, D.C., National Academy Press, 58 p.

Peairs, F. J., and Williams, W. D., 1994, The flooding of Temecula: "Act of God or act of man" [abs]: Geological Society of America Cordilleran Section, 90th Annual Meeting, San Bernardino, California, v. 26, no. 2, p. 80.

Poland, J. F., Lofgren, B. E., Ireland, R. L., and Pugh, R. G., 1975, Land subsidence in the San Joaquin Valley, California as of 1972: U.S. Geological Survey Professional Paper 437-H, p. H1–H78.

Shlemon, R. J., 1995, Groundwater rise and hydrocollapse: Technical and political implications of "Special Geologic Report Zones" in Riverside County, California, USA, *in* Barends, F. B. J., Brouwer, F. J J., and Schroder, F. H., eds., Land Subsidence: Proceedings, International Symposium on Land Subsidence: Fifth, International Association of Hydrological Sciences Publication 234, p. 481–486.

Shlemon, R. J., and Davis, P., 1992, Ground fissures in the Temecula area, southwestern Riverside County, California, *in* Pipkin, B. W., and Proctor, R. J., eds., Engineering geology practice in southern California: Association of Engineering Geologists Southern California Section Special Publication No. 4, p. 275–288.

Shlemon, R. J., and Hakakian, M., 1992, Fissures produced both by groundwater rise and by groundwater fall: A geological paradox in the Temecula-Murrieta area, southwestern Riverside County, California, *in* Stout, M. L., ed., Proceedings, Association of Engineering Geologists, 35th Annual Meeting, Long Beach, California: Association of Engineering Geologists, p. 165–169.

Slaff, S., 1990, Bibliography on Arizona earth fissures and subsidence with selected references for other areas: Arizona Geological Survey Open-file Report 90-7, 28 p.

MANUSCRIPT ACCEPTED BY THE SOCIETY JANUARY 29, 1997

Geological Society of America
Reviews in Engineering Geology, Volume XI
1997

Operation of a landslide warning system during the California storm sequence of January and February 1993

Raymond C. Wilson

U.S. Geological Survey, 345 Middlefield Road, MS 998, Menlo Park, California 94025

ABSTRACT

From 1986 to late December 1995, the U.S. Geological Survey and the National Weather Service operated a landslide warning system for debris flows triggered by intense rainstorms in the San Francisco Bay region. The Landslide Warning System tracked storm systems as they approached the region, determined actual rainfall with a network of radio-telemetered rain gauges, compared the rainfall to thresholds for initiation of debris flows, and issued the appropriate public advisories.

A series of intense rainstorms during January 1993 created hazards from landsliding and flooding over much of California. In the San Francisco Bay region, January rainfall was over 200% of normal, triggering debris flows on natural hillslopes and road cuts across Marin, San Mateo, Alameda, Santa Clara, and Santa Cruz Counties. The warning system issued Flash Flood/Debris Flow Watches during the most intense storms on January 13 and 15, 1993. Most debris flows in this area were small and widely scattered, so damage was largely limited to several blocked roadways in mountainous areas. Storm damage was much heavier in southern California, where rainfall amounts were over 350% of normal for January, triggering flash floods and many landslides. This damage prompted inquiries about developing a landslide warning system for southern California.

A number of elements for a landslide warning system already exist in southern California, including quantitative rainfall forecasting and a network of radio-telemetered rain gauges. Regional rainfall thresholds for debris flow initiation, consistent with the climate, topography, and geology of the region, remain to be developed. Such thresholds could probably be developed with a modest investment of research effort and resources.

INTRODUCTION

The Landslide Warning System in the San Francisco Bay region was designed principally to warn of soil-slip debris flows triggered by intense rainstorms. These landslides result from the failure of colluvium and/or weathered bedrock from steep slopes saturated by intense rainfall. The landslide commonly begins as a coherent slide or slump but then mobilizes into a highly fluid slurry (Ellen and Fleming, 1987). The mobilization destroys most of the shear strength of the slide material, allowing it to accelerate down the steep hillslope, reaching velocities of as much as 20 m/s (45 mph). These soil-slip debris flows are generally small in volume (a few hundred cubic meters or less), but the high velocity gives them great destructive power. In fact, these rapidly moving debris flows are one of the most numerous and life-threatening types of landslide in California.

Because they are so fluid, debris flows can continue moving even after reaching the bottom of their original hillslope. Large, highly mobile debris flows can flow into stream channels, mix with runoff from the intense rainfall, and flow downstream as far as several kilometers. Large debris flows can smash homes and other structures, destroy roads and bridges, sweep away cars, knock down trees, and, finally, lay down thick deposits of mud, rock, and other debris where they come to rest, obstructing drainages and roadways.

Another dangerous feature of debris flows is their potential

Wilson, R. C., 1997, Operation of a landslide warning system during the California storm sequence of January and February 1993, *in* Larson, R. A., and Slosson, J. E., eds., Storm-Induced Geologic Hazards: Case Histories from the 1992–1993 Winter in Southern California and Arizona: Boulder, Colorado, Geological Society of America Reviews in Engineering Geology, v. XI.

abundance—a major rainstorm can trigger hundreds to thousands of debris flows in a period of hours. For example, in a single storm in the San Francisco Bay region (described below), densities of more than 10 to 20 debris flows per square kilometer (26 to 52 per square mile) were observed over large areas, with local densities of as much as $50/km^2$ ($130/mi^2$) (Wieczorek et al., 1988). The cumulative impact of such high concentrations of landslides over large areas can be devastating to roads, power and phone lines, and other lifelines. A road extending even a few kilometers through an area with landslide concentrations of more than $10/km^2$ ($26/mi^2$) probably would be intersected by multiple landslides, making closure of the road a virtual certainty. Communities in mountainous areas may be isolated for as long as several days after a major storm, making relief or rescue difficult or impossible.

Poststorm investigations suggest that people who are alert to their surroundings have a greater chance of surviving when debris flows impact and destroy structures (e.g., Campbell, 1975, p. 29–31). Most fatalities from debris flows occur when occupants of impacted structures are sleeping or otherwise unaware of danger. Acting on a warning of danger thus improves the chance of survival. If evacuation plans and other coordinated response activities are undertaken by public agencies, loss of life and property can be further reduced. Because debris flows occur abruptly and move swiftly, public warnings, to be effective, must be provided in real time as a major storm develops or approaches.

DEVELOPMENT OF THE WARNING SYSTEM

The storm disaster of January 3–5, 1982, in the San Francisco Bay region

A catastrophic rainstorm over the San Francisco Bay area in January 1982 deposited nearly half of the normal annual rainfall in 32 hr and triggered more than 18,000 landslides, principally debris flows, that caused 25 fatalities and $66 million in property damage (Ellen and Wieczorek, 1988). Although the National Weather Service (NWS) had forecast intense rainfall and issued several special weather statements, the destructiveness of the debris flows and other landslides triggered by the storm was unexpected. Following this disaster, the U.S. Geological Survey (USGS), in cooperation with the NWS, began to develop a system for warning the public when rainfall conditions reach or approach critical levels for triggering debris flows.

Development of rainfall thresholds for debris flows

Campbell (1975, p. 31) proposed a debris-flow warning system for the Santa Monica mountains in southern California and provided thresholds of 254 mm (10 in) prestorm seasonal rainfall and continuous rainfall intensity of more than 6.35 mm/hr (0.25 in/hr). Caine (1980) collected a worldwide set of rainfall data recorded near reported occurrences of debris flows and estimated a threshold from the lower bound of a log-log plot of rainfall intensity, I_r (mm/hr), versus the duration, D, in hours, such that: $I_r = 14.82 D^{-0.39}$. Cannon and Ellen (1985) developed thresholds for the San Francisco Bay region, using data from the 1982

storm and several other major storms. They assumed a value of 254 mm (10 in) for the required prestorm rainfall and found that abundant debris-flow activity in the more humid upland areas required storm rainfall with a minimum duration and average intensity of 4 hr at 15 mm/hr (0.6 in/hr), 10 hr at 10 mm/hr (0.4 in/hr), or 20 hr at 8 mm/hr (0.3 in/hr).

After studying a small (12 km^2 [3,000 acres]) area near La Honda, in San Mateo County, that appears to be especially susceptible to debris flows, Wieczorek (1987) estimated the threshold as a minimum duration, D = (9.0 mm)/(I_r – 1.7 mm/hr), of continuous rainfall equal to or exceeding the specified intensity, I_r. Wieczorek also noted the requirement of a minimum amount of prestorm seasonal rainfall, estimated as approximately 280 mm (11 in) for La Honda.

Improving rainfall forecasting

The NWS, meanwhile, developed procedures for issuing quantitative precipitation forecasts throughout northern and central California, based on a combination of weather satellite imagery and large-scale computer models that simulate the global atmospheric circulation. The NWS also coordinated the development of a network of radio-telemetered rain gauges throughout the San Francisco Bay region, based on the Automated Local Evaluation in Real Time (ALERT) system (Fig. 1). As part of this network, the USGS installed an ALERT rain gauge and a number of shallow (30 to 140 cm [12 to 55 in]) piezometers on a hillslope in the La Honda study area that had produced debris flows in several storms.

The first advisories

These developments formed the basis for a debris-flow warning system that was formally initiated in February 1986, when two public warnings were issued through the NWS radio broadcast system, during a sequence of intense storms that triggered hundreds of debris flows in the San Francisco Bay region, causing one fatality and approximately $10 million in property damages (Keefer et al., 1987). These were the first public warnings of debris-flow hazards issued for any region in the United States and accurately predicted the times of major debris-flow events (Keefer et al., 1987, p. 925).

OPERATION OF THE LANDSLIDE WARNING SYSTEM

When a storm approached the San Francisco Bay region, the regional NWS Forecast Office (WSFO San Francisco) prepared a quantitative forecast of storm rainfall. The USGS Landslide Initiation and Warning Project in Menlo Park then compared the observed and forecast rainfall to thresholds for debris-flow initiation. The two groups conferred frequently to assess the probable hazard from debris flows, so that appropriate public statements could be issued (Wilson et al., 1993).

Forecasting the rainfall

Most rainfall in the San Francisco Bay region is produced by Pacific weather systems that originate either in the Gulf of Alaska

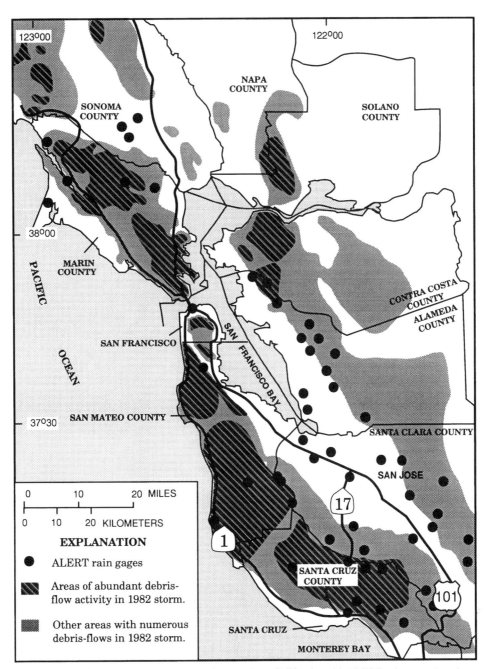

Figure 1. Map of the San Francisco Bay region, northern California, with ALERT rain gauge locations and areas of debris-flow activity during the January 3–5, 1982, rainstorm.

or in subtropical latitudes near Hawaii. In the January 1982 storm, intense and extremely prolonged rainfall resulted from a collision of air masses from both regions. The principal tool for tracking Pacific storms has been the imagery from weather satellites, primarily the GOES (Geostationary Operational Environmental Satellite) series. A GOES satellite positioned over the Pacific transmits frequent images of cloud cover over most of the eastern Pacific, extending from the Gulf of Alaska to the Dateline to the west coast of South America. The spatial patterns of the clouds and their movements, revealed by time-lapse sequencing of sev-

eral images, allow the estimation of speed, direction, and intensity of large storm systems. Imagery in the infrared spectrum indicates the temperatures of the cloud tops, providing important inferences about the expected intensity of rainfall.

Surface and upper-air weather observations, including barometric pressure, wind velocity, temperature, and precipitation, from a network of land-based weather stations, combined with reports from aircraft and ships, also furnish important data on approaching storm systems. Computer simulations of long-term weather trends from the NWS National Meteorological Center in

Camp Springs, Maryland, provide additional forecast guidance. These computer simulations, based on models of global atmospheric circulation, are updated frequently with surface and upper-air observations from throughout the Northern Hemisphere.

At the NWS Forecast Office, the lead forecaster compiles this information and prepares the Quantitative Precipitation Forecast (QPF). The QPF, issued twice daily, estimates the amount of rainfall expected in each of four 6-hr periods, for the following 24 hr, at 17 reference points throughout northern and central California, including a point near the southern tip of San Francisco Bay. The QPF is expressed in terms of rainy day ratios (RDRs), because various phenomena, principally the orographic effect, lead to wide variations in local precipitation amounts. The RDR for a given location is defined as the mean rainfall for the month divided by the mean number of rainy days (days with more than 2.5 mm [0.1 in] rainfall) in that month (Barbato, 1987).

Observing the rainfall

The ALERT system was designed to collect automatic measurements of high-intensity rainfall at remote locations and telemeter this data to central receiving stations for observation and analysis in a near real-time environment. By 1995, there were more than 60 rain gauges in the ALERT network in the San Francisco Bay region (Fig. 1). Although the network was sponsored by the NWS, the individual ALERT stations were purchased, installed, and maintained by a number of other federal, state, and local government agencies.

Each ALERT station is a self-contained unit consisting of a tipping-bucket rain gauge, a power supply, an electronic data-processor, and a radio transmitter. When an amount of rain equivalent to a 1 mm (0.04 in) depth is collected by the rain gauge, the tipping-bucket mechanism engages, tips out the accumulated water, and closes a circuit that increments a data register and prompts the radiotelemetry system to transmit a binary-coded sequence, consisting of the station identification code and the total number of 1-mm (0.04-in) rainfall increments accumulated during the season. This signal may be received and processed by anyone with the requisite radio receiver, microcomputer, and software for data collection, analysis, and display. The USGS maintained an ALERT receiver and dedicated microcomputer data-processing system at its laboratory in Menlo Park, California.

Rainfall thresholds for debris-flow initiation

The warning system had to consider two complementary thresholds that relate to different time scales (Campbell, 1975; Cannon and Ellen, 1985): (1) an antecedent threshold, requiring an accumulation of a certain amount of rainfall during the season, and (2) a storm threshold, requiring that a critical combination of rainfall intensity and duration be exceeded during the course of the storm.

The antecedent rainfall threshold exists because hillside soils in the California coast ranges become dehydrated during the course of the summer dry season, which extends from late April through early October. Some amount of rainfall is necessary to replenish soil moisture, rehydrate clay minerals, and reduce capillary suctions in the soil to levels at which gravitational drainage can take place. Until soil moisture is restored, the positive pore pressures necessary for slope failure cannot form and debris flows are unlikely, even in intense rainfall.

The USGS used two methods to determine whether soil moisture had attained the antecedent threshold. First, seasonal rainfall totals were tracked for ALERT gauges across the Bay area; 254 to 381 mm (10 to 15 in) were required (Cannon and Ellen, 1988). Second, a network of tensiometers and shallow piezometers was monitored at the La Honda study area, which served as a guideline for the region. Soil moisture was considered to have reached the antecedent level when the soil tension first dropped below a critical amount (equivalent to a negative head of −50 cm [2 in] of water). This generally occurred somewhat before the seasonal rainfall total at La Honda reached the antecedent value of 280 mm (11 in) that was determined empirically by Wieczorek (1987).

Once the antecedent threshold was exceeded, approaching storms were evaluated to see if the intensity and duration of the expected rainfall were sufficient to trigger debris flows. The 1986 debris-flow warnings were based on empirical rainfall thresholds that vary over a significant range of values and predict different degrees of debris-flow activity (Keefer et al., 1987). In 1989, these empirical thresholds were consolidated into a pair of relationships between the duration and cumulative amount of peak rainfall bursts (Fig. 2), which together outline a spectrum of debris-flow activity. The lower, "safety" threshold was adapted from Wieczorek's (1987) threshold for the initiation of individual debris flows in the La Honda study area to represent a rainfall level below which significant debris-flow hazards are considered unlikely. The upper, "danger" threshold was adapted from the threshold of Cannon and Ellen (1985), which is based on a comparison of the January 1982 storm with previous storms in the San Francisco Bay area, to represent a rainfall level above which abundant debris flows are likely to occur across broad areas.

A further modification of the threshold levels incorporated orographic effects and other local variations in precipitation by expressing the threshold levels in terms of RDRs. This also facilitated the evaluation of forecast rainfall, which was already expressed in RDRs. In order to compare RDR threshold levels with ALERT observations, the thresholds were converted to absolute rainfall values by multiplying by the rainy-day normal for the ALERT station. Such a conversion, for La Honda, is shown by the scale on the right side of Figure 2.

Issuing debris-flow hazard statements

As a storm entered the San Francisco Bay region, the ALERT network of radiotelemetered rain gauges was used to monitor the rainfall intensities and estimate the speed of advance of the storm front. Observed rainfall amounts, combined with QPF estimates, were compared to the warning thresholds (Fig. 2) to determine the level of hazard and the type of public statement

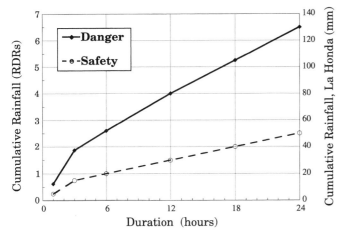

Figure 2. Rainfall thresholds for triggering debris flows in the San Francisco Bay region, expressed as cumulative rainfall of peak rainfall periods of various durations. The left axis is expressed in rainy-day ratios (RDRs) and allows the thresholds to be normalized for orographic effects and other local influences. The right axis is calibrated in millimeters for the La Honda ALERT station (rainy-day normal for La Honda is approximately 20 mm [0.79 in]).

to be issued. Both the NWS and the USGS participated in this phase of the operation.

Storms with peak rainfall periods that fell below the lower threshold were considered unlikely to trigger hazardous debris flows and generally required no statements. For storms with rainfall levels just above the lower threshold, a brief statement was added to an NWS Urban and Small Streams Flood Advisory, warning motorists that roadways might be obstructed by rock falls or debris flows. If rainfall was forecast to approach the upper threshold, a Flash Flood/Debris Flow Watch was issued, advising people living on or below steep hillsides or near creeks to stay alert and be prepared to evacuate, as debris flows were considered a strong possibility during the watch period.

Storms exceeding the upper threshold may trigger hundreds to thousands of debris flows, leading to loss of life and substantial property damage. Therefore, when rainfall was observed to exceed the upper threshold, or if reports of significant debris-flow activity were received, the strongest statement—a Flash Flood/Debris Flow Warning—was issued. Sample texts for these debris-flow statements had been prepared, with wording agreed upon by both the USGS and NWS, so that timely, informative advisories with complete, relevant information could be issued with a minimum of preparation time.

Summary of debris-flow advisories before 1993

After the first public warnings during the storm sequence of February 1986, the Landslide Warning System issued a number of advisories over the next several years. These included (1) a Flash Flood/Debris Flow Warning issued on March 24, 1991, when brief, intense rainfall triggered a large rock fall that closed Highway 17 in the Santa Cruz Mountains; (2) several advisories issued for the area stripped of vegetation by the Oakland fire of October

20, 1991, using a special warning threshold that combined zero antecedent rainfall and reduced intensity-duration levels; and (3) a Flash Flood/Debris Flow Watch issued on February 11, 1992, when rainfall levels of 80 to 120% of the danger threshold triggered numerous debris flows in a small rural area of southwestern San Mateo County.

THE 1993 STORMS IN THE SAN FRANCISCO BAY REGION

Rainfall amounts

Rainfall totals for the month of January 1993 were high, although they attained only about half the record totals of 1862 reported by Null (1992). The NWS rain gauge at San Francisco International Airport (SFO) recorded 286 mm (11.26 in) of rainfall during the month, which is 242% of normal January rainfall. In San Jose, January rainfall for 1993 was 178 mm (7 in), 233% of normal; at the Oakland Museum, 221% of normal; and in Santa Cruz, 213% of normal for January. February totals were also higher than normal: at SFO, 145% of normal; at San Jose, 220% of normal; and at Santa Cruz, 167% of normal.

Landslide advisories and effects

The storm of January 13 was the most intense of the 1993 storms in the Bay area. Early that morning, based on the NWS forecast, the Landslide Warning System issued a Flash Flood/Debris Flow Watch for the entire San Francisco Bay area. Although the combination of rainfall intensity and duration never reached the danger threshold required for a Warning advisory, the storm did trigger a number of debris flows in several areas. Post-storm field reconnaissance located a number of small, widely scattered debris flows on roadways and natural slopes in the East Bay Hills in Alameda and Contra Costa Counties and the southern Santa Cruz Mountains in Santa Cruz and Santa Clara Counties (S. D. Ellen, written communication, 1993).

According to news accounts, debris flows from the storm contributed to a number of road closures. In Contra Costa County, Interstate 680, San Pablo Dam Road, Port Chicago Highway, and Dougherty Road were all closed by debris flows and accompanying flooding. Niles Canyon Road and Crow Canyon Road were among the road closures in Alameda County. At one point in the storm, 25 roads were closed in Santa Cruz County, either from landsliding (at least six) or flooding; 15 roads remained closed overnight.

On the afternoon of January 13, Solano County authorities ordered 30 homes evacuated in Sandy Beach, a small, unincorporated community at the base of a cliff on the east shore of San Pablo Bay. Sandy Beach had suffered significant property damage from landslides from the cliff in the 1982 storm, and officials feared that additional landslides might be triggered by the 1993 rains. A particular concern was that the only road into the community might be blocked, preventing escape or rescue. Most residents, however, refused to leave, even though several small earth flows and debris flows had already occurred. No loss of life or serious injuries occurred.

Several other intense rainstorms passed over the Bay area during the rest of January and February. An additional Watch was issued on January 15, 1993, as well as a number of lesser advisories. On several occasions, bands of intense rainfall were observed with intensities capable of reaching the danger threshold in only a few hours. These bands moved through the region quickly, however, so the durations were too brief to trigger abundant debris flows. In retrospect, the San Francisco Bay region had a series of narrow escapes. With only a minor change in behavior, any one of these storms could have triggered hundreds of debris flows and caused considerable destruction.

THE 1993 STORMS IN SOUTHERN CALIFORNIA

Rainfall amounts

In southern California, monthly rainfall totals for January 1993 were much higher than normal. At Los Angeles International Airport (LAX), for example, the total recorded by the NWS gauge was 270 mm (10.63 in) compared to a normal January total of 78 mm (3.06 in), yielding 347% of normal for the month. Palomar Observatory, in San Diego County, recorded a total of 850 mm (33.4 in) for the month—584% of normal for January and more than the mean annual rainfall of 739 mm (29.10 in). Other gauges also reported very high January totals in 1993: 362% at Sepulveda Dam, 341% at Mt. Wilson, and 430% at Tustin Irvine Ranch. February totals were also high, although not so extreme: 139 mm (5.48 in) at LAX, 220% of normal; 305% of normal at Palomar; and 280% of normal at Tustin Irvine Ranch.

Within the storm sequence of January-February 1993, there were two periods of concentrated flash flooding and landslide activity in southern California: January 15 through 18 produced landslide activity predominantly in Orange County, and February 18 through 22 produced debris flows and other landslides in the Santa Monica Mountains and Mount Washington neighborhood in Los Angeles (Barrows et. al., 1993). Peak rainfalls at a number of gauges in the region (Fig. 3) during these storm periods are listed in Tables 1 and 2. There was an earlier period of intense rainfall on January 6 and 7, but little flooding or landsliding was reported, perhaps because seasonal rainfall totals in the region were still short of antecedent thresholds necessary for slope failure.

Landsliding

Damage from landsliding during the January-February 1993 storms in southern California was surveyed and described by the California Division of Mines and Geology (CDMG). Except where otherwise cited, the information in this section is taken from the CDMG report by Barrows et. al. (1993) and uses the system of locality numbers (#1–#12 in Fig. 3) used in that report. In total, landslides from the 1993 storms in southern California destroyed 35 homes, damaged 137 others, and, when combined with damage to roadways and utilities, caused at least $30 million in property damage. Most of this damage appears to have been concentrated in Orange and Los Angeles Counties.

The largest landslide triggered by the 1993 storms was in Anaheim Hills, Orange County (#1 in Fig. 3). Minor cracking had been observed on a dip slope in upper Miocene marine sandstone and siltstone the previous April, after intense rainfall in February 1992. On January 17, 1993, following intense rainfall since late December, an area of 0.23 km^2 (57 acres) failed as a translational slide and began moving steadily at a rate of 2 to 3 cm (0.8 to 1.2 in) per day. The city responded by evacuating 46 homes and beginning a dewatering program by drilling more than 100 wells into the slide mass. In mid-April 1993, after 45,000 to 57,000 m^3 (12 to 15 million gallons) of water had been removed, the slide appeared to stop moving, but three homes had already been condemned and nine others severely damaged.

On January 18, a small debris slide from the ocean bluff along the border between San Clemente and Dana Point temporarily closed a part of Pacific Coast Highway (#3 in Fig. 3). Following further intense rains in February, on the 22nd a 100-m (328-ft)-long section of bluff collapsed as a large slump, destroying four homes and damaging four others (see Goodman and Darras, this volume). Debris from the slump blocked both the Pacific Coast Highway and Santa Fe Railroad tracks, interrupting railroad passenger service between Los Angeles and San Diego for two weeks.

Elsewhere in Orange County, a slope failure on January 18 destroyed three homes in the Mystic Hills neighborhood of Laguna Beach (#4 in Fig. 3). Barrows et al. (1993, p. 125) describe this failure as "a remobilized old landslide and/or fill failure on a steep canyon wall along a dip slope in Miocene sandstone." Later, on March 12, a slump in Laguna Beach destroyed two homes on Buena Vista Way and Canyon View Road (#5 in Fig. 3). In San Clemente (#2 in Fig. 3), intense rainfall on January 17 through 19 produced debris flows and erosion of cut slopes along the coastal hillsides, damaging over 100 homes and destroying at least two (23 were initially posted as unsafe for entry).

Also in mid-January, numerous debris flows, earth flows, and rock slides were triggered in canyons along the western slope of the Santa Ana Mountains in eastern Orange County (#6 in Fig. 3). One home was destroyed and two others damaged in Mojeska Canyon, and a stable was destroyed in Santiago Canyon. This area has a prior history of debris-flow problems (Campbell, 1975, p. 40). For example, Mojeska and Santiago Canyons, suffered destructive debris flows during a similar series of storms in January and February 1969. In nearby Silverado Canyon on February 25, 1969, five people were killed and 20 injured when a debris flow swept through a fire station that was being used as an emergency shelter (Campbell, 1975, p. 42).

In Los Angeles County, the most damaging landslides from the 1993 storms were in the Castellammare Mesa neighborhood of Pacific Palisades (#7 in Fig. 3), built on an emergent coastal terrace (see Johnson, this volume). In mid-January, large earth flows destroyed three homes, damaged several others, and caused intense damage to public roadways. In February and

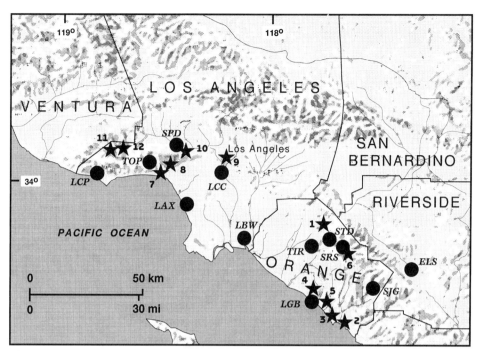

Figure 3. Map of areas in southern California affected by landsliding during the January-February 1993 storm sequence. Solid circles indicate rain gauges (key to abbreviations in Tables 1 and 2); stars indicate locations of reported landslide activity (see text).

TABLE 1. STORM RAINFALL, MAXIMA, SELECTED RAIN GAUGES IN SOUTHERN CALIFORNIA, JANUARY 15–18, 1993*

Station	1 Hour		3 Hours		6 Hours		12 Hours		24 Hours	
	(mm)	(in)	(mm)	(in)	(mm)	(in)	(mm)	(in)	(mm)	(in)
LCP, Lechuza Pt.	18	0.71	20	0.80	38	1.50	43	1.70	53	2.10
TOP, Topanga Patrol Sta.									122	4.80
SPD, Sepulveda Dam	14	0.56	26	1.03	33	1.31	52	2.03	83	3.26
LCC, L.A. Civic Center	8	0.31	13	0.52	17	0.66	27	1.08	42	1.67
LAX, Los Angeles WSO	7	0.28	14	0.28	19	0.73	26	1.03	34	1.34
LBW, Long Beach WSO	7	0.28	14	0.28	21	0.81	31	1.23	37	1.46
TIR, Tustin Irvine Ranch										
STD, Santiago Dam	19	0.75	31	1.23	38	1.50	45	1.77	71	2.78
SRS, Silverado Ranger Sta.	11	0.43	20	0.78	33	1.28	58	2.28	79	3.11
LGB, Laguna Beach 2	13	0.50	18	0.71	23	0.90	38	1.50	56	2.20
ELS, Elsinore	10	0.40	23	0.90	33	1.30	38	1.50	56	2.20
SJG, San Juan Guard Sta.	13	0.50	23	0.90	28	1.10	46	1.80	71	2.80
Temecula	18	0.70	46	1.80	71	2.80	102	4.00	130	5.10
Oceanside Pump Sta.	13	0.50	20	0.80	30	1.20	46	1.80	71	2.80
Palomar Observatory	23	0.90	53	2.10	61	2.40	112	4.40	157	6.20

*Rainfall originally measured in inches; metric conversion rounded to nearest mm.

March, slumps destroyed several homes in the Agoura Hills (#11 and #12 in Fig. 3), in the Mt. Washington district (#9 in Fig. 3), and along the northern slopes of the eastern Santa Monica Mountains (#109 in Fig. 3).

Intense rainfall on February 22 and 23 triggered several debris flows from the steep sides of Mandeville Canyon in the central Santa Monica Mountains (#8 in Fig. 3), damaging two homes. Historically, this has also been a susceptible area. An intense rainstorm on January 25, 1969, triggered a number of debris flows in the same general area, destroying a number of homes and causing one fatality in Mandeville Canyon and several others in nearby Topanga Canyon (Campbell, 1975, p. 40).

Historical precedents

The 1993 winter storms in southern California have clear historical precedents. As noted above, Campbell (1975) describes a similar, but more intense, series of storms in January and February 1969, in which dozens of lives were lost and hundreds of

TABLE 2. STORM RAINFALL, MAXIMA, SELECTED RAIN GAUGES IN SOUTHERN CALIFORNIA, FEBRUARY 18–22, 1993*

Station	1 Hour		3 Hours		6 Hours		12 Hours		24 Hours	
	(mm)	(in)	(mm)	(in)	(mm)	(in)	(mm)	(in)	(mm)	(in)
LCP, Lechuza Pt.	18	0.70	33	1.30	38	1.50	58	2.30	64	2.50
TOP, Topanga Patrol Sta.									69	2.70
SPD, Sepulveda Dam	21	0.84	34	1.32	50	1.97	91	3.58	105	4.12
LCC, L.A. Civic Center	12	0.48	28	1.09	35	1.38	47	1.84	63	2.49
LAX, Los Angeles WSO	12	0.46	24	0.93	25	1.00	31	1.24	34	1.33
LBW, Long Beach WSO	7	0.29	18	0.71	20	0.79	27	1.08	54	2.13
TIR, Tustin Irvine Ranch									54	2.14
STD, Santiago Dam										
SRS, Silverado Ranger Sta.	18	0.71	22	0.87	38	1.48	54	2.14	82	3.22
LGB, Laguna Beach 2										
ELS, Elsinore	8	0.30	18	0.70	28	1.10	41	1.60	51	2.00
SJG, San Juan Guard Sta.	10	0.40	23	0.90	38	1.50	56	2.20	74	2.90
Temecula	10	0.40	23	0.90	38	1.50	58	2.30	64	2.50
Oceanside Pump Sta.										
Palomar Observatory	20	0.80	41	1.60	61	2.40	84	3.30	112	4.40

*Rainfall originally measured in inches; metric conversion rounded to nearest mm.

homes destroyed or damaged by landslides in Orange and Los Angeles Counties. Campbell also briefly described damage from debris flows in several other storms in southern California during the periods of February 7 through 19, 1962, and November 14 through December 30, 1965.

Barrows et al. (1993, p. 123) note that landslides from the 1993 storms were unusual in that a high proportion of the damage was from rotational or translational slides and slumps, rather than the soil-slip debris flows that were the predominant cause of death and destruction from storms in 1969, 1978, and 1980. Rainfall warning thresholds developed for debris flows might not have anticipated the slower, deeper-seated movements that took place during the 1993 storms. Because the primary purpose of the Landslide Warning System was to save lives, rather than prevent property damage, the system was focused on fast-moving soil-slip debris flows, which are more likely to cause deaths or injuries than are large slumps or translational slides that move only a few centimeters per hour.

Even though there were no fatalities or serious injuries, the 1993 storms did cause many small debris flows in areas that, in previous years, produced larger debris flows with a number of fatalities. Because continued growth has probably resulted in even higher risk to lives and property in many mountainous areas in southern California, it might be useful to have a warning system that could alert emergency response agencies and the general public when rainfall conditions approach the critical level. This would allow the most susceptible areas to be temporarily evacuated in an orderly fashion. In a future storm, such warnings and response actions could save a number of lives.

DEVELOPING A WARNING SYSTEM FOR SOUTHERN CALIFORNIA

Development of a landslide warning system requires several elements: (1) a capability to reliably forecast intense rainstorms in the region; (2) a real-time system for monitoring rainfall over the region; (3) development of quantitative threshold relations for the intensity and duration of rainfall required to initiate debris flows under local conditions of topography, geology, hydrology, and climate; (4) creation of an administrative system for collecting and analyzing the relevant weather and geologic data, making the decision to issue a warning, and communicating the warning to the public; and (5) preparation by local communities to respond effectively to protect life and property when debris-flow warnings are received.

Much of the infrastructure necessary to develop and operate a landslide warning system is already in place in southern California. Figure 4 shows the distribution of existing ALERT rain gauges in the Los Angles metropolitan area. These ALERT gauges are currently operated by a number of separate county agencies and public utilities; if coordinated as an integrated network, they could provide excellent regional coverage. Although this would require closer cooperation between the various agencies that currently operate ALERT gauges, the additional costs would be modest.

Further, the NWS Forecast Office (WSFO) in Oxnard, with access to National Oceanic and Atmospheric Administration satellite imagery and National Meteorological Center computer models, is a state-of-the-art facility for meteorological forecasting. The Oxnard WSFO installed the Next-generation Radar (NEXRAD) in 1994. NEXRAD is a Doppler radar system, coupled with a mainframe computer, that can measure wind velocity, temperature, cloudiness, and precipitation over a radius of more than 200 km (124 mi) and should provide a significant advance in the reliability and spatial precision of rainfall forecasting in southern California.

Because so many elements are already in place, establishing a landslide warning system in southern California depends largely on solving the principal remaining technical problem—developing rainfall/debris-flow thresholds for the region. Although Campbell

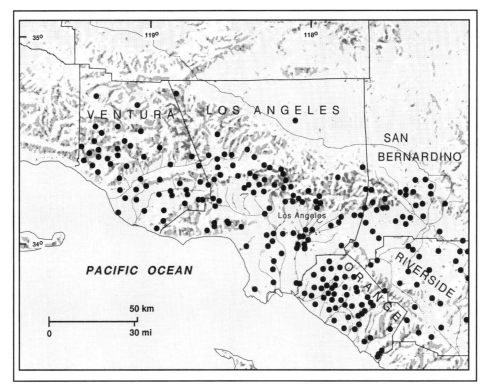

Figure 4. Map of ALERT rain gauge locations in southern California.

(1975) developed preliminary rainfall/debris-flow thresholds for the central Santa Monica Mountains, these thresholds must be updated and extended to a much larger region with a broader range of climatic, topographic, and geologic conditions. This effort would involve the following tasks: (1) compiling historical data on rainfall and landslide occurrence in the region, (2) installing instruments to record fluctuations in soil moisture and pore pressures in representative, vulnerable hillslopes, and (3) analyzing both the historical and instrumental data using simple, idealized hydrological models (e.g., Wilson, 1989), to derive appropriate threshold parameters. This approach has been used to derive thresholds for a proposed debris-flow warning system for Honolulu (Wilson et. al., 1992).

An alternative approach, adapting the thresholds already established for the San Francisco Bay area to southern California conditions, based on an analysis of the climatological differences between the two regions, is discussed in a companion chapter (see Wilson, this volume). Such climatologically adjusted thresholds might be adequate to allow a warning system to function on an interim basis during the several rainfall seasons necessary to collect the instrumental data for more precise thresholds.

Flash-flood and debris-flow advisories for 1993 burn areas

In a sense, a Landslide Warning System for southern California has already begun operation. In the late autumn of 1993, a devastating series of wildfires burned large areas in Los Angeles,

Orange, San Bernardino, Riverside, and Ventura Counties. Historically, severely burned areas in southern California have produced greatly enhanced runoff during subsequent rainstorms and have mobilized large quantities of dry ravel, producing destructive debris flows (Wells, 1987). Intense fires destroy surface vegetation that protects soils from raindrop erosion, loosen surficial soils by desiccation and destruction of organic components, and damage the root systems that help hold the soil on steep slopes. Commonly, organic compounds vaporized from chaparral vegetation may recondense to form layers of hydrophobic (water-repellent) material a short distance (a few centimeters) below the ground surface (Wells, 1987). All of these effects increase the likelihood of excessive erosion or slope failure under intense rainfall.

Recognizing the potential for hazardous floods and debris flows from the burn areas during the approaching winter rainfall season, the California Governor's Office of Emergency Services convened a panel of experts in Pasadena on December 14, 1993, to address the situation. One of the mitigation measures suggested was for the NWS to issue advisories in the event that rainfall conditions were to reach critical levels in the burn areas. After discussion, a consensus was reached on appropriate parameters for rainfall warning thresholds: zero antecedent rainfall and storm rainfall exceeding 25 mm (1 in) in a 6-hour period (R. C. Wilson, meeting notes).

Based on these criteria, the WSFO in Oxnard issued a series of advisories during subsequent rainstorms, including the period of February 6 through 8, 1994, when debris flows caused property damage and forced evacuations in Malibu, Altadena, and Laguna Beach and blocked the Pacific Coast Highway in Malibu (D. Van Cor, NWS, Oxnard, California, written communication, 1994). These experiences provided an unplanned rehearsal of how a Landslide Warning System might actually function in southern California.

Update: Closure of warning system in San Francisco Bay area

In the wake of personnel reassignments, shifting budget priorities, and a major reorganization, the USGS could no longer support the operation of the debris-flow warning system in the San Francisco Bay region. The NWS, citing a lack of expertise in landslide geology, stated that it was unable to assume sole responsibility for the warning system. Consequently, operation was discontinued on December 11, 1995.

ACKNOWLEDGMENTS

The Landslide Warning System in the San Francisco Bay region was operated in close cooperation with the San Francisco WSFO of the NWS, now located in Monterey, California. At the USGS, Robert Mark and Pat Helton also shared in the operation of the Landslide Warning System during the hectic January of 1993. Bob Mark was one of the principal designers of the warning system. In addition to the editors, Robert Larson and James Slosson, Stephen D. Ellen, Douglas M. Morton, Mike Hart, Jerome V. DeGraff, and Scott Burns reviewed the present manuscript; their comments and corrections are greatly appreciated.

REFERENCES CITED

Barbato, G. E., 1987, Quantitative precipitation forecasting in northern and central California by the National Weather Service: Redwood City, California, National Weather Service, 9 p.

Barrows, A. G., Tan, S. S., and Irvine, P. J., 1993, Damaging landslides related to the intense rainstorms of January-February 1993, southern California: California Geology, v. 46, no. 5, p. 123–131.

Caine, N., 1980, The rainfall intensity-duration control of shallow landslides and debris flows: Geografiska Annaler: v. 62A, p. 23–27.

Campbell, R. H., 1975, Soil slips, debris flows, and rainstorms in the Santa Monica Mountains and vicinity, southern California: U.S. Geological Survey Professional Paper 851, 31 p.

Cannon, S. H., and Ellen, S. D., 1985, Rainfall conditions for abundant debris avalanches, San Francisco Bay region, California: California Geology, v. 38, p. 267–272.

Cannon, S. H., and Ellen, S. D., 1988, Rainfall that resulted in abundant debris-flow activity during the storm, *in* Ellen, S. D., and Wieczorek, G. F., eds., Landslides, floods, and marine effects of the storm of January 3–5, 1982, in the San Francisco Bay region, California: U.S. Geological Survey Professional Paper 1434, p. 27–33.

Ellen, S.D., and Fleming, R. W., 1987, Mobilization of debris flows from soil slips, San Francisco Bay region, California, *in* Costa, J. E., and Wieczorek, G. F., eds., Debris flows/avalanches: Processes, recognition, and mitigation: Geological Society of America, Reviews in Engineering Geology, v. 7, p. 31–40.

Ellen, S. D., and Wieczorek, G. F., 1988, Landslides, floods, and marine effects of the storm of January 3–5, 1982, in the San Francisco Bay region, California: U.S. Geological Survey Professional Paper 1434, 310 p.

Keefer, D. K., and 9 others, 1987, Real-time landslide warning during heavy rainfall: Science, v. 238, p. 921–925.

Null, J., 1992, A climatology of San Francisco rainfall [M. S. thesis]: San Francisco, San Francisco State University, 252 p.

Wells, W. G., 1987, The effects of fire on the generation of debris flows in southern California, *in* Costa, J. E., and Wieczorek, G. F., eds., Debris flows/avalanches: Processes, recognition, and mitigation: Geological Society of America Reviews in Engineering Geology, v. 7, p. 105–114.

Wieczorek, G. F., 1987, Effect of rainfall intensity and duration on debris flows on central Santa Cruz Mountains, California, *in* Costa, J. E., and Wieczorek, G. F., eds., Debris flows/avalanches: Processes, recognition, and mitigation: Geological Society of America Reviews in Engineering Geology, v. 7, p. 23–104.

Wieczorek, G. F., Harp, E. L., Mark, R. K., and Bhattacharyva, J., 1988, Debris flows and other landslides in San Mateo, Santa Cruz, Contra Costa, Alameda, Napa, Solano, Sonoma, Lake, and Yolo Counties and factors influencing debris-flow distribution, *in* Ellen, S. D., and Wieczorek, G. F., eds., Landslides, floods, and marine effects of the storm of January 3–5, 1982, in the San Francisco Bay region, California: U.S. Geological Survey Professional Paper 1434, p. 133–161.

Wilson, R.C., 1989, Rainstorms, pore pressures, and debris flows: A theoretical framework, *in* Sadler, P. M., and Morton, D. M., eds., Landslides in a semiarid environment: Riverside, California, Inland Geological Society, v. 2, p. 101–117.

Wilson, R. C., Torikai, J. D., and Ellen, S. D., 1992, Development of rainfall warning thresholds for debris flows in the Honolulu District, Oahu: U.S. Geological Survey Open-File Report 92-521, 45 p.

Wilson, R. C., Mark, R. K., and Barbato, G. E., 1993, Operation of a real-time warning system for debris flows in the San Francisco Bay area, California, *in* Shen, H. W., Su, S. T., and Wen, F., eds., Hydraulic engineering '93: Proceedings, 1993 Conference, Hydraulics Division, American Society of Civil Engineers, San Francisco, California, July 25–30, 1993, volume 2: New York, American Society of Civil Engineers, p. 1908–1913.

MANUSCRIPT ACCEPTED BY THE SOCIETY JANUARY 29, 1997

Geological Society of America
Reviews in Engineering Geology, Volume XI
1997

Broad-scale climatic influences on rainfall thresholds for debris flows: Adapting thresholds for northern California to southern California

Raymond C. Wilson
U. S. Geological Survey, 345 Middlefield Road, MS 998, Menlo Park, California 94025

ABSTRACT

A Landslide Warning System (LWS) operated in the San Francisco Bay region until late 1995. The LWS issued public advisories when rainfall conditions reached or approached critical levels for triggering debris flows ("mudslides"). Interest in an LWS for southern California was revived by the destructive landslides triggered by the storms of January and February 1993 and by the debris-flow problems created by the extensive areas burned in large wildfires the following autumn. Although a number of elements for an LWS already exist in southern California, a critical element must still be developed: the "threshold," a defined set of values of rainfall intensity and duration that predicts debris-flow initiation within a specified region.

Although reliable rainfall/debris-flow thresholds exist for the San Francisco Bay region, climatic dissimilarities between there and southern California produce differences in the thickness, character, and behavior of the hillslope materials that necessitate adjustment of the thresholds. Of particular importance are the amount and distribution of precipitation, which, along the California coast, are controlled by elevation, distance from the coastline, and storm frequency. Storm frequency, in turn, is strongly correlated with geographic latitude. Although storms are less frequent in southern California, with a consequent decrease in mean annual precipitation, average rainfall amounts for individual storms generally equal those of storms farther north.

A procedure is developed for modifying existing rainfall/debris-flow thresholds to account for these changes in precipitation patterns. Then, a set of interim rainfall/debris-flow thresholds is derived for the greater Los Angeles region. As a demonstration, these interim thresholds are compared with data on rainfall and debris-flow occurrence during January and February 1993.

INTRODUCTION

This chapter is a companion to a separate discussion (Wilson, this volume) of the operation of the Landslide Warning System (LWS) in the San Francisco Bay region and the prospect of developing a similar system for southern California. The LWS is a procedure for issuing public advisories before or during periods when rainfall conditions reach critical levels for triggering debris flows ("mudslides") or other shallow landslides that could pose a threat to life and property. Development of such a system for

southern California had been a subject of discussion for a number of years (e.g., Campbell, 1975) but was given a new urgency by the destructive landslides triggered by the storms of January and February 1993 and the debris-flow problems created by large wildfires that burned extensive areas the following autumn.

Although debris flows occur during or immediately after a period of excessive rainfall, other types of landslides, such as deep-seated slumps or slides, may exhibit a delayed reaction in which significant movement occurs days, weeks, or even months later. These delayed reactions may hamper or confuse a warning system

Wilson, R. C., 1997, Broad-scale climatic influences on rainfall thresholds for debris flows: Adapting thresholds for northern California to southern California, *in* Larson, R. A., and Slosson, J. E., eds., Storm-Induced Geologic Hazards: Case Histories from the 1992–1993 Winter in Southern California and Arizona: Boulder, Colorado, Geological Society of America Reviews in Engineering Geology, v. XI.

focused on synchronous rainfall forecasts and observations. Fortunately, these delayed landslides usually move more slowly than debris flows and are therefore less hazardous to personal safety. More traditional forms of mitigation may be more appropriate for these types of landslides.

An essential element of a debris-flow warning system is the "threshold," a defined set of values of rainfall intensity and duration that predicts debris-flow initiation within a specified region. Reliable thresholds developed for the San Francisco Bay region formed the backbone of the operation of the LWS there (Wilson et al., 1993).

Why not simply apply the thresholds already developed for the San Francisco Bay area to southern California? The reason is that rainfall/debris-flow thresholds vary widely with changes in climate, vegetation, and geologic and topographic conditions (e.g., Wilson et al., 1992; Larson and Simon, 1993). Both the San Francisco Bay region and the region surrounding Los Angeles embrace a wide range of all these variables. Compared with the San Francisco Bay region, southern California has a generally drier, warmer climate as well as regions of higher, steeper topography and a similar variety of bedrock geology. Of these differences, the climatic contrast is probably the most important.

This chapter discusses regional, long-term climatic influences on rainfall thresholds and uses this broad-scale understanding to adapt existing thresholds, developed for the San Francisco Bay region, to southern California. These adapted thresholds provide preliminary estimates of thresholds that could serve southern California until verified or modified by local data.

EXISTING RAINFALL THRESHOLDS FOR DEBRIS FLOWS

Campbell (1975) proposed that many rainfall-triggered debris flows in southern California are actually shallow landslides that remobilize into debris flows. These landslides are initiated by a loss of shear strength resulting from an increase in pore pressure, which is, in turn, created by intense rain falling on permeable surficial soils overlying soils or bedrock with reduced hydraulic conductivity. If the rate of rainfall infiltration from the surface exceeds the rate of percolation into underlying materials, then a temporary zone of saturation will develop, increasing the pore pressure on a potential slide plane, until it reaches a critical level and a slope failure is initiated. Campbell (1975, p. 20) proposed a value of 6.4 mm/hr (0.25 in/hr) as a preliminary estimate of this minimum rainfall intensity "for the greater Los Angeles area."

In addition to intense storm rainfall, a certain amount of antecedent rainfall appears necessary for the initiation of debris flows. Campbell (1975, p. 20) noted the requirement of "an initial period of enough rainfall to bring the full thickness of the soil mantle to field capacity (the moisture content at which, under gravity, water will flow out as fast as it flows in)." Campbell cited a value equivalent to 254 mm (10 in) for the initial rainfall requirement and noted that the initial requirement may be more

closely associated with total seasonal rainfall than with rainfall shortly before the storm.

Since Campbell's work, several other investigators have published empirical estimates of the intensity and duration of rainfall required to trigger debris flows. Caine (1980) collected a worldwide set of rainfall data recorded near reported occurrences of debris flows and derived a rainfall/debris-flow threshold by fitting a lower bound to a log-log plot of peak intensities versus duration. Cannon and Ellen (1985) developed rainfall thresholds for the San Francisco Bay region, based on lower-bound combinations of rainfall intensity and duration from several large historical storms, principally the January 1982 storm that triggered numerous debris flows throughout the region. An empirical intensity/duration threshold was also developed for the highly susceptible La Honda study area, based on rainfall measurements and debris-flow observations collected over a period of 9 yr (Wieczorek, 1987).

The latter two thresholds formed the basis for the thresholds used in the LWS in the San Francisco Bay region (Wilson et al., 1993): The "danger" threshold is adapted from the Cannon and Ellen (1985) threshold for abundant debris flows over wide areas and the "safety" threshold is adapted from Wieczorek's (1987) relation for individual debris flows in a small, highly susceptible area. The companion chapter (Wilson, this volume) discusses the use of these thresholds to issue appropriate advisory statements.

In developing thresholds for the San Francisco Bay area that could be used on a regional scale, a thorny problem arose. Because it is a coastal region with significant relief, the San Francisco Bay region exhibits significant local climatic variations due to orographic effects, distance from coastline, slope aspect, prevailing winds, and so forth. How do these effects influence the rainfall required to trigger debris flows? Would different thresholds have to be devised for each individual rain gauge? How can rainfall on a susceptible hillslope be estimated if the nearest rain gauge has a different orographic setting? Can systematic relationships be developed that allow the debris-flow thresholds to be "normalized," to correct for orographic effects and other local variations in storm precipitation?

Initially, Cannon and Ellen (1985) separated the historical rainfall data into two groups on the basis of whether the mean annual precipitation (MAP) in the area of the rain gauge was above or below 660 mm (26 in). Cannon (1988) subsequently refined this concept by dividing the storm rainfall intensity recorded at a given gauge by the MAP of that gauge, then used these data to prepare a normalized debris-flow threshold.

Continuing this idea, Wilson et al. (1993) normalized the "danger" and "safety" thresholds by expressing them in terms of rainy-day ratios (RDRs), which are used by the National Weather Service (NWS) to correct for orographic effects in their quantitative precipitation forecasts. Initially, thresholds expressed as RDRs were considered equivalent to those normalized by MAP. Although this assumption now appears incorrect, as discussed below, it can be tolerated on a regional basis but will produce substantial errors when one compares regions with significantly different climates.

TWO MEASURES OF PRECIPITATION: MAP AND RDN

Climatologists use a number of parameters to describe the precipitation of an area. By far the most common is the mean annual precipitation (MAP), the total precipitation for the year averaged over a number of years. The MAP is useful for studies of vegetation, groundwater recharge, agriculture, and other applications dealing with the total water budget for the year.

A less common precipitation parameter is the average rainfall for rain days—days in which rain exceeds some minimum amount (e.g., Linacre, 1992, p. 287–288). Because of its close correlation with the maximum precipitation expected for some specified period, this parameter is useful for studies in which the amount of precipitation in a single storm event is important. Linacre (1992, p. 288) notes, for example, "There is a clear relationship between the average rainfall per rainday in the USA and the daily rainfall likely to be exceeded only once in two years."

In northern California, the NWS defines a "rainy day" as one with a minimum precipitation of 2.54 mm (0.1 in). For a given station (rain gauge), the rainy-day normal (RDN) is computed by dividing the mean monthly precipitation by the mean number of rainy days in the month (Barbato, 1987). The RDN thus reflects how much rain is expected on a rainy day for a given month at a particular station. For most stations in California, the RDN is approximately constant for the three wettest months (December, January, and February), and in the following discussion RDN refers to this value unless otherwise specified.

In its quantitative precipitation forecasts, the NWS predicts rainfall amounts for each 6-hr period in the following 24 hr, then divides these amounts by the RDN, yielding normalized rainy-day ratios (RDRs). As explained below, this procedure allows adjustment of the forecast amounts for local climatic variations such as the orographic effects produced by the complex topography of the region.

CLIMATIC DIFFERENCES BETWEEN NORTHERN AND SOUTHERN CALIFORNIA

General climate of the Pacific coast

The broadscale, long-term climatic patterns of winter rainfall on the Pacific coast of the United States are related to a system of perennial features of the atmospheric circulation over the North Pacific Ocean. An area of low pressure, called the Aleutian Low, is generally centered southwestward of Alaska. An area of high pressure, called the East Pacific High, is usually located off the Pacific coasts of Mexico and Central America. These long-term barometric features are superimposed on the global zonal atmospheric circulation, which produces a zone of eastward flowing air, called the westerlies, between the latitudes of 30° and 60° N. This system tends to move southward in the winter, then northward again in the summer.

Most precipitation is produced by storms associated with low-pressure systems. As near-surface air flows in toward the cen-

ter of the low, convergence forces it to rise and cool, producing condensation and precipitation. Conversely, high-pressure centers mark places where a high-altitude air mass is subsiding and thereby warming and lowering its relative humidity. As a result, rainfall tends to be intensified in areas of low pressure and suppressed in areas of high pressure.

During the summer, storms traveling eastward to the California coast are usually blocked by the East Pacific High, which has moved into its northerly position off Baja California. During the winter, the high retreats southward, opening the storm path, while low-pressure systems (cyclones) spawned in the far North Pacific and the Gulf of Alaska travel southeastward toward the California coast. These large, long-lived features of the atmospheric circulation—Aleutian Low, East Pacific High, and westerlies—and their seasonal movements combine to control the gross distribution of precipitation in California: wet winters, dry summers, and a general decrease in the amount of precipitation southward from the Oregon border to Mexico.

Factors influencing precipitation on the California coast

The climates of northern and southern California are similar, in that both receive almost all of their precipitation from Pacific frontal systems during the winter months. However, the MAP in southern California is approximately half of that in the San Francisco area. The MAP at a location along the California coast is determined by three factors: (1) the elevation of the site, (2) the distance from the coastline, and (3) the average number of storms during the winter season, which appears to be strongly correlated with geographic latitude.

The first factor, elevation, influences average rainfall through orographic effects. As a Pacific storm passes inland, the moist marine air is forced to rise from near sea level to the height of the local ground surface, which may rise to hundreds or thousands of meters within a few tens of kilometers from the coastline. This abrupt increase in elevation subjects the air mass to adiabatic cooling, causing increased precipitation. For any individual storm, other factors may complicate this orographic process, including convergence and convection (e.g., thunderstorms), but for a long-term average, higher elevation generally implies higher precipitation. For example, Pasadena at an elevation of 265 m (869 ft) has an MAP of 490 mm (19.3 in), whereas nearby Mount Wilson at an elevation of 1,740 m (5,709 ft) has an MAP of 860 mm (33.9 in). (All values of MAP cited here are from National Climatic Data Center, 1981.)

The second factor, distance from the coastline, affects average precipitation because the marine moisture from Pacific storm systems is depleted through precipitation as the storms move inland. For a given latitude and elevation, the farther a site is from the coast, the larger the loss from previous precipitation and, in general, the lower the average precipitation. This effect is exaggerated if an area of higher elevation lies between the coastline and the site under consideration, resulting in a "rain shadow" effect. As an example, we again look at the Pasadena gauge, which is 35 km

(22 mi) from the coastline, with a MAP of 490 mm (19.3 in), and compare it to the gauge at Riverside Fire Station #3, which is 66 km (41 mi) inland, with a MAP of only 245 mm (9.6 in). The two gauges have similar elevations—265 mm (869 ft) and 256 m (840 ft), respectively.

The third factor, frequency of winter storms, is largely constrained by the broad atmospheric circulation patterns in the North Pacific, described above, and varies with the latitude of the site. For example, the average number of rainy days (days with more than 2.54 mm [0.10 in] of rainfall) per year is 22 for San Diego (Lat. 32.7° N), 40 for Half Moon Bay (Lat. 37.5° N), and 72 for Crescent City (Lat. 41.8° N) (Weaver and Denney, 1969). The variation in storm frequency is illustrated in more detail in Figure 1, which plots the ratio, MAP/RDN, against the latitude from San Diego (32° N) to the Oregon border (42° N) for a sample of 34 rain gauges near the Pacific coast. When the MAP is divided by the RDN for winter months, the resulting ratio is a relative measure of the frequency of winter rainy days. The MAP/RDN ratio increases markedly from south to north up the coast (from left to right on Fig. 1).

Classical models of global atmospheric circulation (e.g., Lutgens and Tarbuck, 1992, p. 185–187) predict that precipitation in temperate latitudes will vary from a minimum at 30° N to a maximum at 60° N. By modeling this variation as a function of the cosine of six times the latitude (LAT), a regression line,

$$\frac{MAP}{RDN} = 101 + 88\cos(6\,LAT), \qquad (1)$$

can be fit closely to the data in Figure 1.

Recently, Spencer (1993) mapped global variations in oceanic precipitation from satellite microwave measurements. Spencer's maps indicate broad plumes of higher MAP in both the Pacific and Atlantic, extending from lower to higher latitudes and trending northeastward in the Northern Hemisphere or southeastward in the Southern Hemisphere. Along the axis of the North Pacific plume, MAP decreases gradually from 3,800 mm (150 in) off southern Japan to 2,100 mm (83 in) off British Columbia, then decreases more steeply to the southeast along the coast of North America, to a minimum of 230 mm (9 in) off Baja California. With no orographic effects over the open ocean, MAP should correlate with the frequency of storms. In any case, the relationship between storm frequency and latitude along the California coast is reasonably well described by Eq. 1, as shown in Figure 1.

Summary—Fewer, not drier, rainy days in southern California

The highest elevations in the greater Los Angeles region—3,000 m (10,000 ft)—exceed those in the San Francisco Bay area—1,100 m (3,600 ft)—so that orographic effects should be greater in the south, yielding more precipitation, not less. Both regions are bounded by the sea coast and extend about 60 km (37.3 mi) inland. This leaves the third factor, the reduced frequency of winter rainy days as one moves south in latitude, as the

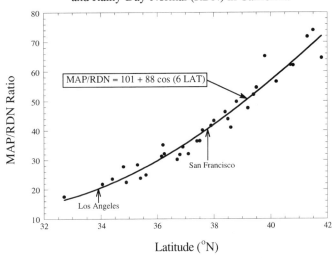

Regional Variation in Mean Annual Precipitation (MAP) and Rainy-Day-Normal (RDN) in California

Figure 1. Plot of the ratio of mean annual precipitation (MAP) to rainy-day normal (RDN) (for December through February), versus latitude, for 31 rain gauges along the California coast from San Diego (Lat. 32.7° N) to Crescent City (Lat. 41.8° N). The ratio is an index of the frequency of winter rainy days. The MAP data are taken from the National Climatic Data Center (1981); the RDN data (Barbato, 1987) are for December-January-February and were estimated by the NWS California–Nevada River Forecast Center, using the procedure of Weaver and Denney (1969).

principal reason that the Los Angeles region is significantly drier than the San Francisco Bay area.

Indeed, the MAP/RDN relationship shown in Figure 1 suggests that the southern climate is drier principally because of *fewer* days of rain rather than because of days with *lesser* amounts of rainfall. For example, Los Angeles International Airport, near the coast and close to sea level, has a MAP of 307 mm (12.08 in), whereas a similar coastal station in the San Francisco Bay region, Half Moon Bay, has a MAP more than twice as high, 641 mm (25.22 in); yet the two stations have similar RDNs of 15 mm (0.60 in) and 17.5 mm (0.69 in), respectively. Similarly, the San Diego Weather Service Office (WSO) gauge, where MAP = 237 mm (9.32 in), is much drier than the gauge at the San Francisco Federal Building, where MAP = 491 mm (19.33 in); yet the two RDNs are nearly identical, 13.5 mm (0.53 in) and 14 mm (0.55 in), respectively. So, although the MAP for southern California sites will only be about half that of similar sites in the San Francisco Bay region, they should have approximately equal RDN values.

Estimation of rainy-day normals for southern California

Because Barbato (1987) was concerned primarily with precipitation forecasts in northern California, he lists RDN values for many rain gauges in northern California but only a few for gauges in southern California. However, the relation depicted in Figure 1 may be used to estimate RDN values for rain gauges in southern California by using Equation 1 to estimate the MAP/RDN ratio from the latitude (LAT) of the station, then multiplying this ratio by the MAP of the gauge, so that

$$RDN = MAP(\frac{1}{MAP/RDN}) = MAP(\frac{1}{101 + 88\cos(6\,LAT)}). \quad (2)$$

Table 1 lists values of latitude, MAP, and estimated RDN values for several southern California rain gauges.

A GENERIC RAINFALL THRESHOLD FOR DEBRIS FLOWS

Before considering how these climatic factors are likely to influence the rainfall intensity/duration thresholds for debris-flow initiation, the process by which intense rainfall triggers slope failures will be reviewed briefly, using Campbell's (1975) conceptual model, as further developed by Wilson (1989). In this model, debris flows begin as soil slips, triggered by elevated positive pore pressures created by intense rainfall ponding in a zone of saturation perched above a permeability contrast within the hillslope materials.

Antecedent rainfall requirement

Early in the rainfall season, the hillslope materials (colluvium and weathered bedrock, hereafter referred to as regolith) have been dehydrated by evaporation and transpiration during the long dry season in summer and fall. Any remaining soil moisture is held under strong negative pore pressures (soil suctions). Until this moisture deficit is restored by early seasonal rainfall, conductivity will be slow, and high soil suctions will prevent the formation of the positive hydrostatic pore pressures necessary for slope movement. Thus, debris flows are very unlikely early in the rainfall season, even if early storms are severe.

Campbell (1975, p. 20) described the antecedent rainfall requirement as "an initial period of enough rainfall to bring the full thickness of the soil mantle to field capacity (the moisture content at which, under gravity, water will flow out as fast as it flows in)." However, as noted by Johnson and Sitar (1987, p. 13), such a description "ignores the process of soil drainage and moisture redistribution" between rainfall events. Perhaps a better description of the antecedent rainfall requirement might be: that amount of distributed seasonal rainfall necessary to replenish the moisture in the soil profile to a level such that additional rainfall will infiltrate above the perching layer faster than the water can drain away, creating a zone of saturation within the regolith. To achieve this antecedent moisture content, a sufficient amount of rainfall must infiltrate and accumulate in the regolith while overcoming losses to evaporation, transpiration, and drainage.

The total amount of seasonal rainfall required depends on the antecedent moisture content, the losses to evapotranspiration, and the thickness of material that must be rehydrated. The antecedent moisture content depends on the mineralogy, texture, and degree of

TABLE 1. MEAN ANNUAL PRECIPITATION (MAP) AND RAINY-DAY-NORMAL (RDN) VALUES FOR SELECTED RAIN GAUGES IN SOUTHERN CALIFORNIA*

Rain Gauge	Latitude (°N)	MAP (in)	MAP (mm)	RDN (in)	RDN (mm)
Lechuza Point	34.08	22.12	562	1.06	27
Topanga Patrol Station	34.08	24.79	630	1.19	30
Sepulveda Dam	34.17	16	406	0.75	19
Los Angeles Civic Center	34.05	14.85	377	0.71	18
Los Angeles WSO (LAX)	33.93	12.08	307	0.59	15
Long Beach WSO	33.82	11.54	293	0.58	15
Tustin Irvine Ranch	33.73	11.97	304	0.61	15
Santiago Dam	33.78	20	508	1.01	26
Silverado Ranger Station	33.75	20	508	1.02	26
Laguna Beach 2	33.55	12.34	313	0.65	17
Elsinore	33.67	11.66	296	0.6	15
San Juan Guard Station	33.60	16	406	0.83	21
Temecula	33.50	15	381	0.8	20
Oceanside Pumping Plant	33.22	12	305	0.67	17
Palomar Observatory	33.35	29.1	739	1.58	40

*Latitudes and MAP values from National Climatic Data Center, 1981; RDN values estimated using Equation 2.

compaction of the regolith materials. The evapotranspiration losses are highly variable but are generally minimized during the early and middle part of the winter rainfall season by low temperatures, short periods of daylight, and relatively dormant vegetation. (Evapotranspiration increases rapidly during the spring months when temperatures and daylight hours increase, and the grasses and other annuals reach their peak growth periods.)

The weathering rate is influenced by a number of factors, including the mean soil temperature, vegetation, and soil microbiology, but most strongly by the total amount of moisture available during the year, controlled primarily by the mean annual precipitation. Thus, the MAP becomes the predominant climatic influence on the amount of seasonal rainfall required to put the soil profile into the antecedent moisture condition necessary for slope failure.

Retaining a critical amount of rainfall in the hillslope

Once the antecedent moisture condition is satisfied, then additional rainfall can, if retained in the hillslope, build up a zone of saturated soil that generates positive pore pressures. If the zone of saturation becomes sufficiently thick, then hydrostatic pore pressures will rise to a level that leads to slope movement. Thus, the failure of a slope by heavy rainfall requires that the slope retain a certain critical amount of that rainfall, here denoted as Q_c.

Although it is conceivable that a brief, but very intense, rainstorm could deposit an amount of rainfall just equal to Q_c on the hillslope and trigger a debris flow, this situation would require the slope to have an unusual combination of very high infiltration capacity, so that all of the rainfall would be absorbed, and very slow drainage, so that all of the rainfall would be retained. Hillslopes susceptible to debris flows generally do have a high infiltration capacity, but they also tend to drain rapidly, so that a significant amount of rainfall is likely to be lost during the duration of a storm. Thus, retention of rainfall within the hillslope depends on a dynamic balance between the rate of infiltration and the rate of drainage. Generally, an amount of storm rainfall well in excess of Q_c will be required to produce a debris flow on such slopes. Therefore, the rainfall threshold is not simply a constant rainfall total equal to Q_c but is composed of a set of inversely related combinations of rainfall intensity and duration necessary to overcome the drainage while retaining a rainfall amount equal to or greater than Q_c.

Idealized model for debris-flow thresholds

The dynamic interaction between infiltration and drainage will be rather complex in any actual field situation, but its gross features can be simplified as follows: (1) Since the hillslope soils most vulnerable to debris flow generally have high infiltration capacities, the infiltration rate is assumed to equal rainfall intensity (although some time lag may be present); and (2) the drainage rate is proportional to the amount of rainfall already retained in the hillslope. Using these assumptions, and the further assumption of a relatively uniform rainfall intensity, Wilson (1986) developed a simple, one-dimensional, mass-balance model (also described in Keefer et al., 1987) that expresses the rainfall intensity/duration thresholds in the form

$$(I_r - I_o) D = Q_c, \qquad (3)$$

where I_r is the rainfall intensity averaged over the rainfall duration (D), I_o is the average rate of drainage, and Q_c is the amount of rainfall stored within the soil column when slope failure is imminent. The parameters I_r and D are used to describe the rain storm; the parameters Q_c and I_o describe the hillslope properties relevant to slope failure.

Wilson (1989) developed this model further, using a numerical algorithm that calculated the changes in the level of water in a leaking barrel that received rainfall at the top but drained out at the bottom at a rate proportional to the water level in the barrel. In this model, the drainage is described in terms of a drainage coefficient, k_d, or an equivalent drainage half-life ($T_h = ln(2)/k_d$). Wilson used this "leaky-barrel model" to broaden the previous assumption of uniform rainfall intensity.

In January 1982 a storm stalled over the San Francisco Bay region and produced nearly constant rainfall intensities for periods of more than 18 hr, but such stationary fronts are very unusual in this region. Most Pacific coast rain storms are associated with moving frontal systems in which the rainfall intensity increases rapidly as the front approaches, reaches a maximum, then decreases rapidly after the front passes. This pattern was modeled as a "triangular burst," in which the rainfall intensity increases linearly with time from zero to a maximum value, then decreases linearly back to zero (Wilson, 1989). Under these conditions, the rainfall/debris-flow threshold becomes

$$R_t = Q_c + C k_d Q_c D, \qquad (4)$$

where R_t = total rainfall produced by the rainfall burst; Q_c, k_d, and D are defined as above; and C = a dimensionless geometric term equal to 0.48 (Wilson, 1989, p. 110).

In fact, this relation is equivalent in form to Equation 3, but is expressed in terms of cumulative rainfall, R_t, instead of averaged intensity, I_r, so that $R_t = I_r D$, and

$$R_t = Q_c + I_o D. \qquad (5)$$

Thus, the average rate of drainage, I_o in Equation 3 is equivalent to

$$I_o = C k_d Q_c. \qquad (6)$$

INFLUENCE OF CLIMATE ON RAINFALL/ DEBRIS-FLOW THRESHOLDS

The effects of climatic differences may be estimated, in a preliminary way, by using the generic rainfall/debris-flow threshold (Equation 5) to compare two hypothetical slopes, of equal steepness and underlain by similar materials. One slope is located in the San Francisco Bay region; the other is in southern California. The critical retained rainfall, Q_c in Equations 3 and 5, is influenced by the thickness, texture, and density of the hillslope materials. Although the precise value of the proportionality between regolith thickness and Q_c is unknown, it should be similar for the two regions.

Estimating the likely effect of regional climate on the drainage rate, I_o, is less straightforward and requires a move from a simple one-dimensional model of the soil profile on a hillslope to a more complex, multidimensional model of an entire low-order drainage basin, including a network of stream channels for surface runoff. Under low or moderate rainfall conditions, the hillslope soil moisture remains below saturation, and drainage is dominated by unsaturated flow, with little or no surface runoff. Under intense rainfall conditions, however, assuming that the regolith is more permeable than the underlying bedrock, the hillslope soils become saturated, and the drainage is dominated by shallow throughflow delivered to channels. Under these storm conditions, the drainage rate will be linked to the spatial density of ephemeral surface channels, termed the drainage density.

In Carlston's (1963) statistical study of the relation between stream discharge and physiography, he found a strong correlation between the square of the drainage density and the mean annual flood runoff in 15 basins in the eastern United States. Carlston concluded that "drainage density is adjusted to the most efficient removal of flood runoff" and that this equilibration is accomplished by events roughly equivalent to the mean annual flood (return period 2.23 yr).

As already noted, the daily rainfall likely to be exceeded only once in a 2-year period (in the United States) is closely correlated with the RDN, a measure of the strength of a "typical" storm (Linacre, 1992, p. 288). It is thus likely that the rainfall event that equilibrates surface drainage also corresponds to some (unknown) multiple of the RDN. If so, then, to a first approximation, the drainage rate, I_o, should be proportional to RDN, and the climatic adjustment for this term becomes

$$(I_o)_s = (I_o)_n \frac{(RDN)_s}{(RDN)_n}, \qquad (7)$$

where the notation "$(\ )_s$" denotes southern California, and "$(\ )_n$" denotes northern California.

Incorporating these estimated adjustments for Q_c and I_o into Equation 5, the complete formula for climatic adjustment of the rainfall intensity/duration thresholds for debris-flow initiation becomes

$$(R_t)_s = Q_c + D(I_o)_n \frac{(RDN)_s}{(RDN)_n}. \qquad (8)$$

Because the MAP/RDN ratio is approximately constant for a given value of latitude (Fig. 1), a formula normalized by either MAP, as in Cannon (1988), or by RDN, as in Wilson et al. (1993), would work acceptably well within a narrow range of latitude. Over a broader range of latitude, such as between the San Francisco Bay region and Los Angeles, however, the MAP/RDN ratio shifts significantly and normalizing by MAP alone will produce significant errors in the rainfall warning thresholds.

RENORMALIZED DEBRIS-FLOW THRESHOLDS FOR SOUTHERN CALIFORNIA

To illustrate how thresholds can be adjusted for climatic differences, two sites are selected for comparison, one from the San Francisco Bay region, where rainfall thresholds have been determined, and one from southern California. The site chosen to represent the San Francisco Bay region is the La Honda study area, with MAP = 750 mm (29.5 in) and RDN = 20 mm (0.8 in). The normalized rainfall/debris-flow thresholds used at this site and others in the San Francisco Bay region (Wilson et al., 1993) were adapted from thresholds defined on an empirical basis, but values of Q_c and I_o in Equation 5 can be found, using a modified regression analysis, that yield values of R_t versus duration that closely fit these empirical values for durations of 3 hr or more. This analysis results in the following parameters: Q_c = 30 mm (1.18 in) and I_o = 4.167 mm/hr (0.16 in/hr) for the danger threshold, and Q_c = 10 mm (0.39 in) and I_o = 1.667 mm/hr (0.066 in/hr) for the safety threshold.

The Lechuza Point rain gauge in the Santa Monica Mountains was selected to represent precipitation conditions in southern California. At Lechuza Point, MAP = 562 mm (22.13 in) and RDN = 26.9 mm (1.06 in) (based on Equation 2). Using Equation 7, the parameters for the renormalized danger threshold may be calculated as follows:

$$(Q_c)_s = (Q_c)_n = 30 \text{ mm} (1.18 \text{ in})$$

and

$$(I_o)_s = (I_o)_n \frac{(RDN)_s}{(RDN)_n} = (4.167 \text{ mm/hr}) \frac{(26.9 \text{ mm})}{(20 \text{ mm})}$$
$$= 5.604 \text{ mm/hr} (0.22 \text{ in/hr}).$$

Using a similar procedure for the renormalized safety threshold yields the values $(Q_c)_s$ = 10 mm (0.39 in) and $(I_o)_s$ = 2.242 mm/hr (0.088 in/hr). These parameters, when combined with Equation 8 and converted to RDRs, yield the renormalized thresholds shown in Figure 2.

Comparison of renormalized thresholds and 1993 storm data

Had a warning system been in place in southern California during the 1993 winter storms, how well would the renormalized rainfall warning thresholds have performed? Hourly precipitation data from the 1993 storms were compiled for several southern California rain gauges (National Climatic Data Center, 1993a, 1993b). Using Equation 2, RDNs were estimated for the selected rain gauges (Table 1). Two storm periods were selected: January 15–18, 1993, corresponding to the period when debris flows were generated in the Puente Hills and the Santa Ana Mountains (Barrows et al., 1993), and February 18–22, 1993, corresponding to the period of debris-flow activity in Mandeville Canyon and elsewhere in the Santa Monica Mountains.

Comparison of Renormalized Rainfall Warning Thresholds
for San Francisco Bay Region and Southern California

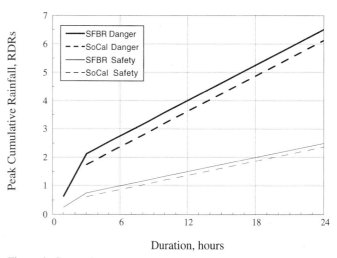

Figure 2. Comparison of renormalized rainfall warning thresholds for southern California (SoCal) with existing thresholds for San Francisco Bay region (SFBR). Graph shows thresholds in terms of cumulative rainfall for peak rainfall periods of various durations, normalized to rainy-day ratios (RDRs), versus the duration of the peak rainfall period in hours. The danger threshold predicts abundant debris flows over wide areas; the safety threshold predicts scattered debris flows in highly susceptible areas.

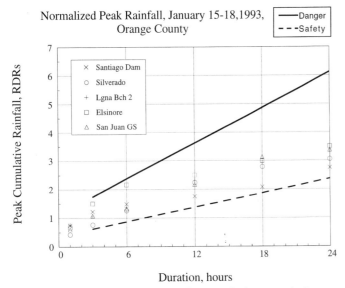

Figure 3. Plot of peak rainfall values for several rain gauges in Orange County during storms of January 15–18, 1993. Rainfall values are normalized to RDRs, using the RDN values in Table 1. Shown for comparison are the renormalized rainfall warning thresholds calculated for southern California.

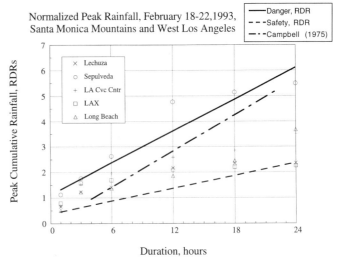

Figure 4. Plot of peak rainfall values for several rain gauges in the Santa Monica Mountains and western Los Angeles during storms of February 18–22, 1993. Rainfall values are normalized to RDRs, using the RDN values in Table 1. Shown for comparison are the renormalized rainfall warning thresholds calculated for southern California. Also shown is Campbell's (1975) threshold, 6.4 mm/hr (0.25 in/hr), normalized to RDRs using the Lechuza Pt. gauge (RDN = 27 mm [1.06 in]).

For the two storm sequences, rainfall data were collected from the subset of rain gauges closest to the areas where debris-flow activity occurred (Wilson, this volume, Tables 1 and 2). The data were reduced to maximum cumulative rainfall amounts for various periods (R_t versus D), normalized to RDRs by dividing by the RDN, and plotted as Figures 3 and 4, along with the renormalized rainfall warning thresholds developed above (Fig. 2).

Figure 3 shows that, of the five rain gauges closest to the debris-flow activity in the Santa Ana Mountains during the storms of January 15–18, only Elsinore exceeded the renormalized "danger" threshold. However, all five of the gauges exceeded the renormalized "safety" threshold. Had the rainfall data been received as forecasts to a warning system, rather than historical records, the system would have predicted that debris flows would occur in this area but at a generally moderate level. Some property damage might have been expected but not at the catastrophic levels of the January 1982 storm in the San Francisco Bay region (e.g., Creasy, 1988) or the January and February 1969 storms in southern California (Campbell, 1975). This prediction would have closely matched the moderate levels of damage that actually occurred in the area: one house destroyed, two damaged in Mojeska Canyon, and a stable partially destroyed in Santiago Canyon (Barrows et al., 1993).

The data plotted in Figure 4 for western Los Angeles and the Santa Monica Mountains during the storms of February 18–22 would have produced a similar prediction—a moderate level of debris-flow activity, with significant, but not catastrophic, damage. However, one rainfall record, Sepulveda Dam, significantly exceeds the danger threshold, indicating that intense debris-flow activity might be possible in upland areas near this rain gage. Barrows et al. (1993) reported several debris flows in nearby Mandeville Canyon, where two homes were damaged by debris and mud.

Comparison of renormalized thresholds to Campbell's (1975) threshold

Also shown in Figure 4 is a line representing the rainfall/debris-flow threshold proposed by Campbell (1975, p. 20) for the Santa Monica and San Gabriel Mountains. Campbell postulated a minimum rainfall intensity of 6.4 mm/hr (0.25 in/hr), for an unspecified duration "lasting long enough to establish a perched groundwater table of sufficient proportional thickness . . . to cause failure." For Figure 4, Campbell's threshold has been converted into cumulative rainfalls, normalized by dividing by the RDN value from Lechuza Point, 27 mm (1.06 in) (Table 1), and plotted for a range of durations from 4 to 22 hr, inferred from Campbell's (1975, his Figure 9) plot of rain-gauge records from the January 18–26, 1969, storm sequence. Inspection of Figure 4 shows that the renormalized danger threshold is in fair agreement with the Campbell threshold, adapted as described, for durations longer than 12 hr.

DISCUSSION

I have described how intense rainfall triggers debris flows; how the climatic precipitation parameters, MAP and RDN, vary with elevation, distance from the coastline, and latitude; and how these broadscale climatic variations can be used to adjust rainfall/debris-flow thresholds. By using Equation 8 to readjust the rainfall/debris-flow thresholds developed for the San Francisco Bay region, rainfall thresholds have been developed for southern California climatic conditions. These readjusted thresholds have been tested against some of the data on rainfall and debris-flow occurrence during the January-February 1993 storm sequence (Figs. 3 and 4). What conclusions can we draw?

Although the data and arguments in this chapter present permissible evidence for the utility of renormalized thresholds for predicting debris-flow activity in southern California, the case is by no means proven. These thresholds should be tested and modified by collecting and analyzing a more extensive set of historical data, similar to the procedure used in the San Francisco Bay region (Cannon and Ellen, 1985; Cannon, 1988).

The thresholds also need firmer geotechnical and hydrologic foundations. Wieczorek and Sarmiento (1988) installed and monitored rain gauges and piezometers at the La Honda study area, the site of frequent historical debris-flow activity. Wilson et al. (1992) made similar measurements in Honolulu in an attempt to develop thresholds for a warning system there. Someday, data from these or similar studies may be used to synthesize rainfall/debris-flow thresholds within the context of a coherent regional model of climatology, hydrology, and geomorphology.

Nevertheless, the renormalized thresholds could serve, on an interim basis, while a Landslide Warning System was being established and firmer thresholds developed. During this time, the system could gain several seasons of operating experience during which storm forecasts, actual rainfall, and debris-flow activity could be compared on a systematic basis and thresholds adjusted accordingly. Should a major storm occur during this interim period, the renormalized thresholds presented above might help a fledgling warning system save a number of lives.

ACKNOWLEDGMENTS

This chapter grew out of several discussions with Jim Slosson over the past few years about the influence of climate on landforms along the California coast. I first learned of Roy Spencer's spectacular precipitation maps of the global ocean in a talk by Daniel Cayan. In addition to the editors, Robert Larson and James Slosson, the present manuscript was reviewed by Stephen D. Ellen, Robert K. Mark, and Susan H. Cannon for the U.S. Geological Survey, and Michael Hart, Jeff Keaton, and Terry West for the Geological Society of America. Their comments and corrections are greatly appreciated.

REFERENCES CITED

Barbato, G. E., 1987, Quantitative precipitation forecasting in northern and central California by the National Weather Service: Redwood City, California, National Weather Service, 9 p.

Barrows, A. G., Tan, S. S., and Irvine, P. J., 1993, Damaging landslides related to the intense rainstorms of January-February 1993, southern California: California Geology, v. 46, p. 123–131.

Caine, N., 1980, The rainfall intensity-duration control of shallow landslides and debris flows: Geografiska Annaler, v. 62A, p. 23–27.

Campbell, R. H., 1975, Soil slips, debris flows, and rainstorms in the Santa Monica Mountains and vicinity, southern California: U.S. Geological Survey Professional Paper 851, 31 p.

Cannon, S. H., 1988, Regional rainfall-threshold conditions for abundant debris-flow activity, *in* Ellen, S. D., and Wieczorek, G. F., eds., Landslides, floods, and marine effects of the storm of January 3–5, 1982, in the San Francisco Bay region, California: U.S. Geological Survey Professional Paper 1434, p. 35–42.

Cannon, S. H., and Ellen, S. D., 1985, Rainfall conditions for abundant debris avalanches, San Francisco Bay region, California: California Geology, v. 38, p. 267–272.

Carlston, C. W., 1963, Drainage density and streamflow: U.S. Geological Survey Professional Paper 422-C, p. c1–c8.

Creasy, C. L., 1988, Landslide damage: A costly outcome of the storm, *in* Ellen, S. D., and Wieczorek, G. F., eds., Landslides, floods, and marine effects of the storm of January 3–5, 1982, in the San Francisco Bay region, California: U.S. Geological Survey Professional Paper 1434, p. 195–203.

Johnson, K. A., and Sitar, N., 1987, Debris flow initiation: An investigation of mechanisms: University of California Geotechnical Engineering Report UCB/GT/87-02, 179 p.

Keefer, D. K., and 9 others, 1987, Real-time landslide warning during heavy rainfall: Science, v. 238, p. 921–925.

Larson, M. C., and Simon, A., 1993, A rainfall intensity-duration threshold for landslides in a humid-tropical environment, Puerto Rico: Geografiska Annaler, v. 75A, p. 13–23.

Linacre, E., 1992, Climate data and resources: A reference and guide: London and New York, Routledge, 366 p.

Lutgens, F. K., and Tarbuck, E. J., 1992, The atmosphere, an introduction to meteorology (fifth edition): Englewood Cliffs, New Jersey, Prentice Hall, 430 p.

National Climatic Data Center, 1981, Climatography of the United States, Number 81: Monthly normals of temperature, precipitation, and heating and cooling degree days 1951–80, California: Asheville, North Carolina, National Oceanic and Atmospheric Administration, Environmental Data and Information Service, National Climatic Center, p. 14–20.

National Climatic Data Center, 1993a, Hourly precipitation data, California, January 1993: Asheville, North Carolina, National Oceanic and Atmospheric Administration, Environmental Data and Information Service, National Climatic Center, v. 43, no. 1, 61 p.

National Climatic Data Center, 1993b, Hourly precipitation data, California, February 1993: Asheville, North Carolina, National Oceanic and Atmospheric Administration, Environmental Data and Information Service, National Climatic Center, v. 43, no. 2, 55 p.

Spencer, R. W., 1993, Global oceanic precipitation from the MSU during 1979–91 and comparisons to other climatologies: Journal of Climate, v. 6, p. 1301–1326.

Weaver R., and Denney, W., 1969, Normalized quantitative precipitation forecasting in California: U.S. Weather Bureau manuscript for 230th National Meeting of the American Meteorological Society, 11 p. (Available from National Weather Service Forecast Office, Monterey, California.)

Wieczorek, G. F., 1987, Effect of rainfall intensity and duration on debris flows on central Santa Cruz Mountains, California, *in* Costa, J. E., and Wieczorek, G. F., eds., Debris flows/avalanches: Processes, recognition, and mitigation: Geological Society of America Reviews in Engineering Geology, v. 7, p. 23–104.

Wieczorek, G. F., and Sarmiento, J., 1988, Rainfall, piezometric levels, and debris flows near La Honda, California, in storms between 1975 and 1983, *in* Ellen, S. D., and Wieczorek, G. F., eds., Landslides, floods, and marine effects of the storm of January 3–5, 1982, in the San Francisco Bay region, California: U.S. Geological Survey Professional Paper 1434, p. 43–62.

Wilson, R. C., 1986, Estimating rainfall required to initiate debris flows: Association of Engineering Geologists, 29th Annual Meeting, San Francisco, Abstracts and Programs, p. 69.

Wilson, R. C., 1989, Rainstorms, pore pressures, and debris flows: A theoretical framework, *in* Sadler, P. M., and Morton, D. M., eds., Landslides in a semi-arid environment: Riverside, California, Inland Geological Society,

v. 2, p. 101–117.

Wilson, R. C., Torikai, J. D., and Ellen, S. D., 1992, Development of rainfall warning thresholds for debris flows in the Honolulu District, Oahu: U.S. Geological Survey Open-File Report 92-521, 45 p.

Wilson, R. C., Mark, R. K., and Barbato, G. E., 1993, Operation of a real-time warning system for debris flows in the San Francisco Bay area, Califor-nia, *in* Shen, H. W., Su, S. T., and Wen, F., eds., Hydraulic engineering '93: Proceedings, 1993 Conference, Hydraulics Division, American Soci-ety of Civil Engineers, San Francisco, California, July 25–30, 1993, Vol-ume 2: New York, American Society of Civil Engineers, p. 1908–1913.

MANUSCRIPT ACCEPTED BY THE SOCIETY JANUARY 29, 1997

Geological Society of America
Reviews in Engineering Geology, Volume XI
1997

Effects of the 1993 storms on the west Castellammare mesa landslide, city of Los Angeles, California

Jeffrey A. Johnson
Department of Geological Sciences, San Diego State University, 5500 Campanile Drive, San Diego, California 92182-4610

ABSTRACT

The storm of January 18, 1993, triggered or reactivated an older landslide that destroyed nearly a dozen homes in the Castellammare mesa area of Los Angeles, California. The catastrophic slope failure was the end result of the 1992–1993 rains and more than 100 years of local development that included construction and maintenance of coastal and local roads, construction of hillside homes, and maintenance of the mesa. Residential development started in the mid-1920s. Unimproved lots were sold and residences constructed, starting in 1926, without consideration of geologic hazards. The presence of large ancient landslides was determined from mapping started in the 1950s. However, lot by lot development continued without proper consideration of regional hazards. Remedial repairs were conducted by the city of Los Angeles, Caltrans, and private home owners in a non-integrated fashion, generally in response to catastrophic failures. Significant slope failures were observed during the rains of 1938, 1941, 1952, 1969, 1978, and 1983. By late 1992, the region had deteriorated significantly because of slope creep and poor maintenance. Site reviews during and following the rains of January 18, 1993, indicated the need for (1) an understanding of regional geologic hazards and geotechnical problems associated with the development on and maintenance of a relatively large, paleolandslide; (2) an integrated, geotechnical approach to the development of an area of small, individually owned lots; and (3) a single government agency working with the home owners' association to coordinate geotechnical studies, local government improvements, development and maintenance of private lots, and the maintenance of streets, utilities, dewatering wells, and other infrastructure.

INTRODUCTION

The rains of January 18, 1993, triggered a massive landslide that destroyed nearly a dozen homes in the Castellammare area of Los Angeles, California (Fig. 1). The catastrophic failures of early 1993 were the end result of more than 100 yr of change that included construction and maintenance of coastal and local roads, residential hillside development, and maintenance of the mesa. To understand the direct effects of the 1993 storms on what will be referred to as the West Castellammare Mesa Landslide (WCML), it is important to review the history of the area and gain an understanding of the events that preceded the January rains. This chapter (1) documents the effects of the rains (including January 18, 1993); (2) provides needed background data, including local geologic conditions; (3) reviews the geotechnical problems associated with the development on and maintenance of a relatively large, paleolandslide; (4) provides a summary of the type and extent of geologic investigations conducted in the area, before and after the event; and (5) presents suggestions for the engineering geologic analysis of small, single-lot developments in complex areas.

The 1993 phase of slope failures started in January 1969 with the reactivation of older or paleolandslides that included destruction of the residence at 17900 Porto Marina Way, failure of

Johnson, J. A., 1997, Effects of the 1993 storms on the west Castellammare mesa landslide, city of Los Angeles, California, *in* Larson, R. A., and Slosson, J. E., eds., Storm-Induced Geologic Hazards: Case Histories from the 1992–1993 Winter in Southern California and Arizona: Boulder, Colorado, Geological Society of America Reviews in Engineering Geology, v. XI.

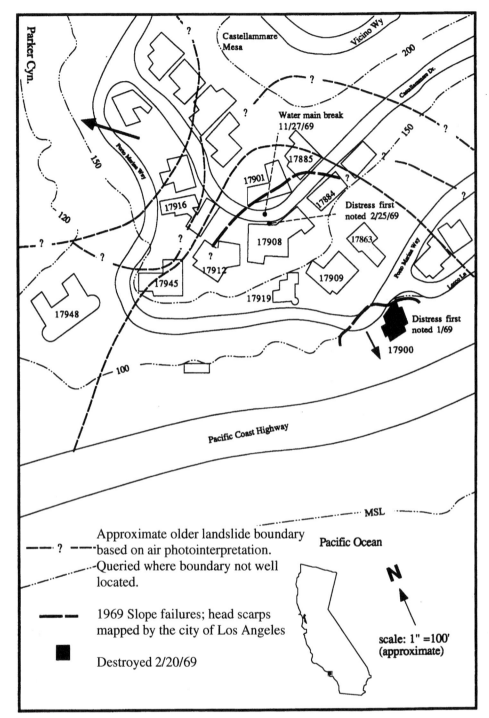

Figure 1. Slope failures and observed distress in the west Castellammare Mesa area of Pacific Palisades, 1969, and photointerpretation of older, preexisting landslides.

a portion of Porto Marina Way, and distress to the street and a number of residences along Castellammare Drive (Fig. 1). The progressive timing of the slope failures, the pattern of cracking, and the location and sequence of utility failures indicate that the 1969 and 1993 failures are part of a complex rock slide. Losses included destruction or significant distress to 12 single-family res-

idences and failure of a number of vacant lots. Mitigation included construction of a $3 million multistreet repair of questionable long term stability. Litigation resulted in the payout of millions of dollars in settlements and fees to landowners, lawyers, and consultants.

The subject area is located in the western part of Castellammare Mesa, Los Angeles, California (Fig. 1). The lower part of the mesa is a series of shallow to deep paleolandslides and recently activated and/or reactivated slope failures. Residential development began in the mid-1920s with the construction of roads and underground utilities. Roads were constructed on or across landslides without geologic review. Excavated rock and soil were pushed from cuts onto natural, unprepared slopes. Surface drainage was designed to be collected in the streets and transported without storm drains. Subsurface drainage was nonexistent until city of Los Angeles road repairs of 1970. Unimproved lots were sold, and homes were, in general, constructed on relatively shallow foundations. Evaluation of real or potential geologic constraints or hazards was not consistently considered in the design of residential foundations or surface-water drainage until the development of updated hillside grading codes in the early 1960s.

My site reviews over the last 27 yr have indicated the need for (1) a clear understanding of regional geologic hazards; (2) an integrated, geotechnical approach to the development of an area of relatively small, individually owned lots; and (3) a single government agency, working with the land owners, to coordinate geotechnical studies, local government improvements, development and maintenance of private lots, and the maintenance of streets, utilities, dewatering wells, and other infrastructure.

The review of the WCML, outlined in this chapter, consists of four parts: review of local geologic conditions, including review of historic air photographs and locally extensive subsurface explorations; mapping of surface cracking and distress to cultural features; review of surface-water and groundwater hydrology; and analysis of historic references and geotechnical reports. The results are then combined in the formulation of a basic understanding or interpretation of the WCML and the effects of the 1993 storms.

LOCAL GEOLOGY

The WCML is located on the south-facing slope below the southwestern rim of Castellammare Mesa (Fig. 1). The general area descends southward toward the Pacific Coast Highway (PCH). Regional geology by Hoots (1930) has recently been remapped by McGill (1982a and 1989) and Dibblee (1992). The upper part of the mesa is capped by a relatively thin layer of marine and nonmarine terrace deposits (Q_t). These deposits rest unconformably on Upper Cretaceous Tuna Canyon Formation (K_t) and lower Miocene Sespe Formation (T_s). McGill (1989) mapped K_t faulted against T_s between PCH and Porto Marina Way. The fault, as mapped by McGill, trends east-west across the slide area, bending to the northwest near the west end of Lecco Lane. Dibblee (1992) shows the fault trending eastward across the entire subject area. Both McGill and Dibblee indicate that the fault zone dips northward. McGill (1989) considers the fault to be a detachment structure. The existence of the faulted rock was confirmed during subsurface explorations noted below. The trace of the fault could not be shown because of the width of the fault zone and its burial by landslide debris.

Since the 1960s the type and extent of subsurface exploration within the WCML have ranged from shallow hand-dug pits to deep,

continuous core borings. Logging has included simple drawings with lithologic notes, downhole logging with a video camera, and most recently Fullbore Formation MicroImager (FMI) logging conducted by Schlumberger (Jeffrey A. Johnson, Inc., 1993). I have been involved in nearly every type of subsurface exploration in the area, including downhole logging of large-diameter, drilled excavations. Each method has its merits, depending on the type of data needed and the local geologic conditions. However, in a zone such as the WCML where deep landslides are occurring in tectonically altered, low-shear-strength materials, the most effective means of exploration is a deep, continuous-core boring supplemented with downhole geophysics. The ability to review core and geophysical logs side-by-side is a powerful method needed to examine and review the origin, depth, and geometry of shear planes.

Parts of an FMI log conducted by Schlumberger at 17885 Castellammare Drive are shown on Figures 2 and 3. The electrical FMI images, a processed structural data (i.e., dip-meter data), and core were used to document local geologic conditions to a depth of about 42.7 m (140 ft). The method allows (1) orientation of cores that are rotated by the drilling and recovery process, (2) a check of depths provided by the drillers, (3) comparison of structural data measured from the cores with the dip meter data, and (4) development of a log of zones of poor or no core recovery.

Each gray scale image shown on Figures 2 and 3 covers ~0.9 m (3 vertical ft) of the boring. The two larger, side-by-side images are identical. In the center of the two images is the scale in feet below ground surface. Along the right side of the right image are the results of the dip-meter calculations. For example "5/169" is printed in the right-hand column at ~27.6 m and 27.99 m (90.6 and 91.8 ft). The "5" is the dip angle, and the "169" is the dip direction in clockwise degrees from north. Lines across the image represent the orientation of the planar features calculated by the dip meter. The images are relatively easy to interpret by geologists who have down-hole logged large-diameter drilled excavations. Each image is a 360° view of the side walls of the boring. Orientation of the image is given at the top of the figure. For analysis, consider the image rolled into a cylinder (image facing inward) with the "0" and "360" degree marks joined. The image on the far right of both figures is a view of what the core would look like at that depth viewed to the northwest in Figure 2 and to the north in Figure 3.

In general the lighter the gray tones the coarser the material (Figs. 2 and 3). Comparison of the image with the core indicates that the rock is highly sheared to brecciated (i.e., tectonic breccia). The relatively light gray, angular fragments are resistant clasts of fine-grained sandstone in a clay matrix (i.e., the darker portion of the image). The breccia appears to be mainly of marine origin and is most likely part of the Tuna Canyon Formation (McGill, 1989). Of importance to the long-term stability of the area are low shear strength and adversely dipping zones similar to that shown at a depth of ~27.4 to 28 m (90 to 92 ft) on Figure 2. The FMI image is extremely valuable because many of the structural details in the critical, soft shear zones (i.e., clay matrix) are lost as the resistant sandstone clasts shift and rotate during the drilling process.

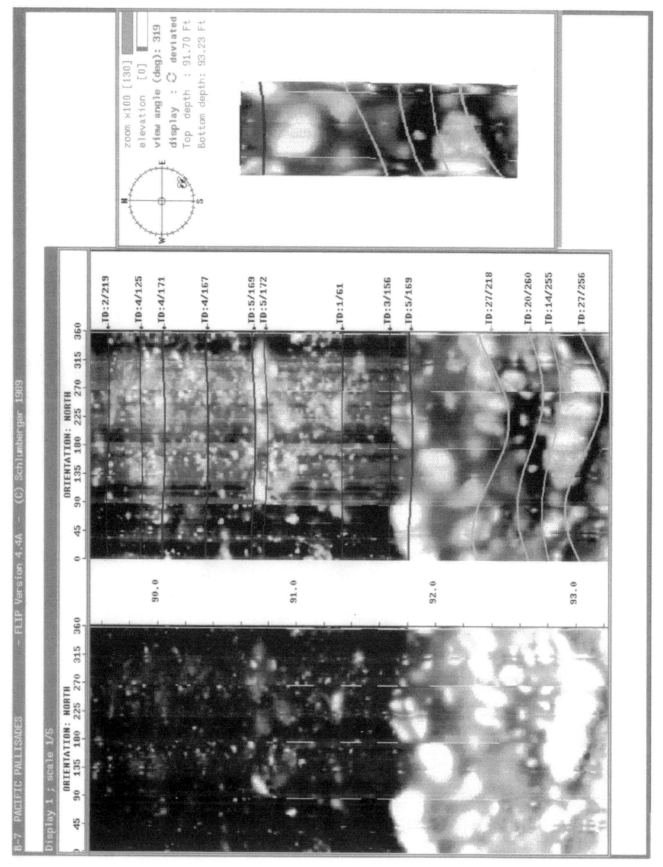

Figure 2. A portion of a Fullbore Formation MicroImager (FMI) log from a deep drilled excavation at 17885 Castellammare Dr. Log shows the interval from approximately 27.13 to 28.35 m (89 to 93 ft). Logging by Schlumberger.

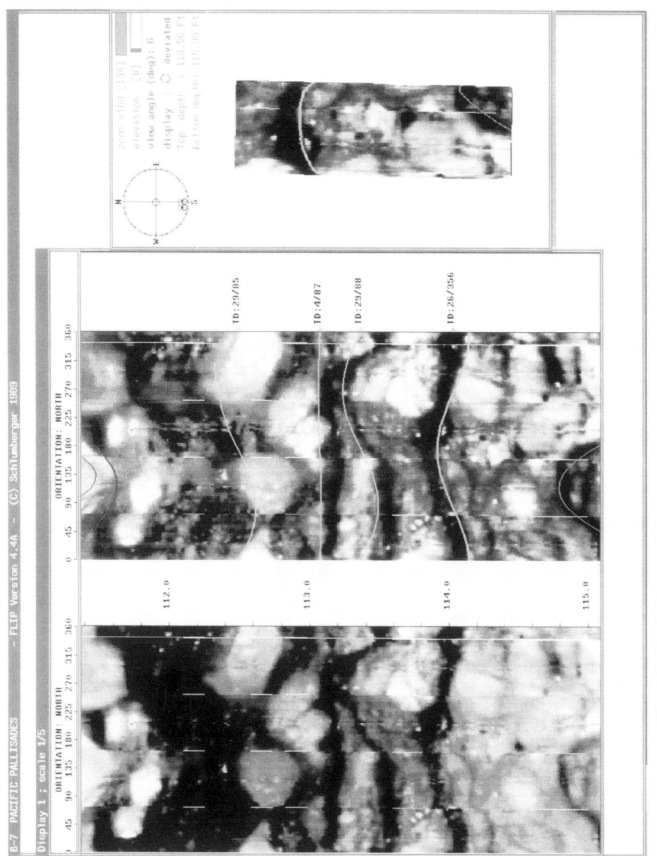

Figure 3. A portion of a Fullbore Formation MicroImager (FMI) log from a deep drilled excavation at 17885 Castellammare Dr. Log shows the interval from approximately 33.84 to 35.1 m (111 to 115 ft). Logging by Schlumberger.

Bedding within the Sespe Formation above and north of 17885 Castellammare Drive dips 12 to 29° southward. The nonmarine, reddish to maroon sandstone was not clearly visible in core from a deep boring on Porto Marina Way west of Lecco Lane. Sespe Formation was observed in borings on top of the mesa, locally in hand-dug trenches near Lecco Lane, and also on the slope above Porto Marina Way west of Lecco Lane. Faulting and/or slope failure(s) may explain the local distribution of Sespe Formation.

Capping the landslide north of Castellammare Drive are ~6.1 m (20 ft) of terrace sediments. Both marine (Q_{tm}) and nonmarine (Q_t) deposits were observed in large-diameter borings. The nonmarine deposits consist of ~5.18 m (17 ft) of slightly moist, red-brown, fine silty sand with clasts. A significant cobble zone was noted at a depth of 3.66 m (12 ft). Q_{tm} consisted of a tan, fine, clean sand, possibly a beach deposit. Terrace deposits, consisting of reddish-brown, fine silty sand, were also observed in a hand-dug excavation north of Porto Marina Way near the west end of Lecco Lane.

Slope stability

Air photographs taken in the 1920s and 1940s provide evidence of a long history of slope failure along the southern and western margins of Castellammare mesa (Fig. 1). The shallow and deep-seated failures nearly mask the slope above PCH. The region affected by the older landslides is larger and more complex than suggested by either McGill (1989) or Dibblee (1992). The slides appear to extend in an east-west direction from near the eastern end of Lecco Lane to the residence at 17948 Porto Marina Way. To the north, topographic evidence of a slope failure was observed south of Vicino Way. Also shown on Figure 1 are a series of possible older landslides on the west-facing slope that descends toward Parker Canyon. Some of the landslides shown on Figure 1 have not moved historically and have not been confirmed by subsurface excavation.

At the time the area was first developed, in the mid-1920s, geologic and geotechnical studies were not required. Roads were cut into and homes were built on older landslide deposits. Not until the heavy rains of 1952 did the city of Los Angeles consider the importance of geotechnical review of hillside developments. Required geologic reviews started in 1963 when modern grading ordinances were enacted (Prevost, 1993).

Local slope instabilities or landslides are associated with the above-normal winter rains of 1940–1941 (83.2 cm [32.76 in]), 1968–1969 (69.8 cm [27.47 in]), 1978–1979 (84.9 cm [33.44 in]), 1982–1983 (79.4 cm [31.25 in]), and 1992–1993 (69.5 cm [27.36 in]) and possibly with road construction along PCH in the late 1920s to mid-1930s (Moran, Proctor, Mueser, and Rutledge, 1959). Failures from the period 1978 to 1983 are shown on Figure 4. Moran, Proctor, Mueser, and Rutledge (1959) reviewed the area for the State of California. Their study was for "the control and correction of landslides which had occurred along Highway 101. . . ." Few of the their recommendations were acted on. Their comments regarding local slope stability included:

1. Removal of large masses of slide talus from the toe by erosion or by highway maintenance operations leads to continued instability of the slide mass. Therefore, as far as practical, the talus that moves onto the shoulder of PCH should remain in place.

2. There appears to be a separation of water levels between a perched zone of seepage and a much lower permanent groundwater table. The lower level is below the bottom elevations of the canyons to the north and west and may be fed from a distant source. The upper water levels, which affect the failure plane, must be derived from local irrigation and runoff. The two merge lower on the slope.

3. Most surface runoff is carried on the streets. High general groundwater levels and concentrated infiltration at the top set the stage for instability. Runoff should be collected and removed to prevent it from entering the sliding masses.

4. The first movements of record are associated with the grading of slopes for the highway realignment of 1933–1935. Although the amount of material removed in the original cuts was limited, continuing maintenance led to the retrogression of the slides to the city street above the highway.

5. Groundwater removal is recommended at both active and prehistoric slide locations by two to four levels of gently sloping hydrager drains.

6. Geologic processes have continued with some acceleration due to the increased supply of water for infiltration in developed areas. Wave cutting and erosion at the base of the sea cliffs have been virtually eliminated by the construction of seaward protection for beaches and the Pacific Coast Highway. The stabilizing effects of this work have been partially offset by removal of failed materials from the toe of active slides in the grading operations.

7. In the majority of slides the direction of the failure zone does not correspond to the dip of beds. . . . Bedding attitude is not a major or even an important factor in the large-scale movements that have been investigated.

8. In areas of potential slides impacting Tertiary materials, the elimination of toe cutting in canyons or on the Pacific Coast Highway combined with subsurface drainage can prevent the formation of new slides and will stabilize the lower portions of existing slides.

The majority of the active slope failures are occurring within a highly sheared and inherently weak tectonic breccia, as noted above. Planes of weakness within the rock are common, dipping at a wide range of angles and directions. Observed shear zones range from dark brown to nearly black slickensided clays to tan to gray silty zones with a relatively high sand content. Because the landslides are within a breccia, shear zones may contain angular clasts, significant in both size and number, of resistant fine-grained sandstone.

Slope inclinometer data

Experience gained over the last few years, including comparing core with slope-indicator (SI) data, indicates that deeper failure surfaces can be clearly identified only if the landslide is moving and the movement can be detected by SI measurements.

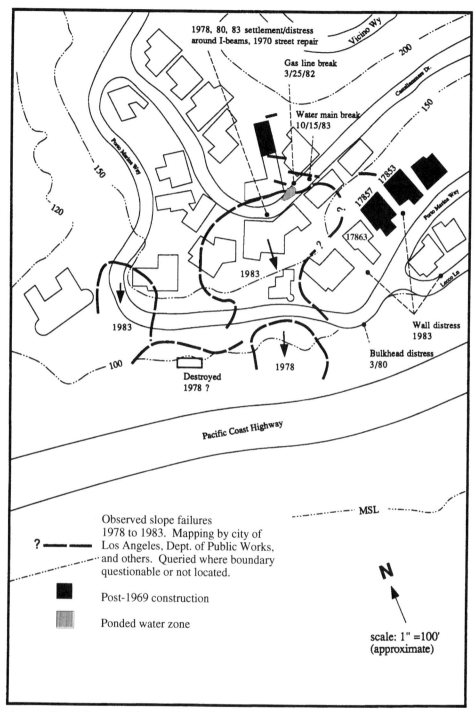

Figure 4. Slope failures and observed distress in the west Castellammare Mesa area of Pacific Palisades, 1978 to 1983.

Bedrock is highly sheared and brecciated. The relatively youthful-looking shear zones cannot be classified with a high degree of confidence by physical examination and structural measurements alone as either of tectonic origin or the result of gravity slope failure. Careful review of geophysical data and core at several different locations are also needed to estimate the lateral extend and depths of these shear zones that must be considered potential failure planes. Failure surfaces of shallow depth can generally be observed in large-diameter borings.

As of May 1993, a total of 11 slope-monitoring stations had been installed and observed within the WCML since the failures of 1969. Clear evidence of movement was noted at nine stations. SI measurements since early 1993 indicate that movement is occurring along at least three and possibly four separate slide planes south of Castellammare Drive. The elevation of the lowest recorded movement was ~20.43 m (67 ft) above mean sea level.

Hydrogeology and surface drainage conditions

Slope failures within the WCML are related to local and regional groundwater conditions and the flow and infiltration of surface water along Castellammare Drive and Porto Marina Way. The timing of historic slope failures correlates with high rainfall seasons and associated infiltration, the rupture of buried water mains, and the infiltration of surface water into shear and tension cracks along streets within the WCML. Groundwater data were obtained from a number of borings drilled between 1967 and 1993. Perched water and generally moist to saturated shear zones generally exist within the upper active secondary landslides, and a probable water table may intersect deeper slide surfaces south of Castellammare Drive. Significant change in water level elevations (10.37 m [34 ft]) was noted along Castellammare Drive between 1976 and 1980. Surface seeps or springs were observed and mapped by McGill (1982b, 1989) and by Geology and Soils Consultants, Inc. (1972) and during our recent regional mapping. McGill (1989) noted seeps along the north side of PCH near the toe of several recent slope failures. Geology and Soils Consultants, Inc. (1972) mapped seeps north of and adjacent to Porto Marina Way.

CHRONOLOGY OF DEVELOPMENT AND SLOPE FAILURES

Five events or series of events have greatly affected the stability of the region: (1) the development, improvement, and maintenance of local roads; (2) residential construction on the slope above PCH starting in the mid-1920s; (3) the rains and slope failures of the early 1940s and 1969; (4) the physical deterioration of streets, homes, and infrastructure between 1970 and late 1992; and (5) the rains of 1992–1993. Earthquakes, such as those in Long Beach in 1933 and in Northridge in 1994, may also have adversely affected regional stability. Data supporting earthquake effects are very limited in the subject area.

Roads

In the mid-1870s a cattle trail and stage road were constructed along the coast north of the city of Santa Monica (Moran, Proctor, Mueser, and Rutledge, 1959). Locally the road was underwater at high tide. In 1906, a 3.05 m (10-ft)-wide county road was constructed along the beach to Topanga Canyon, north and west of the mesa. Starting in 1922, the road was regraded and realigned by the state of California and extended northwestward to Malibu. The result was a 6.1-m (20-ft)-wide concrete strip between Santa Monica and Las Floras Canyon (Moran, Proctor, Mueser, and Rutledge, 1959). Locally, the toe of the slope was cut for the improvement.

During this period, small road-cut failures were noted as several curves on the old road were eliminated by changes in the alignment (Moran, Proctor, Mueser, and Rutledge, 1959).

Between 1932 and 1935, PCH was again improved by excavation at the base of the bluffs and by providing riprap and groins on the beach. Cut slope failures were noted at four or five locations in the city of Los Angeles during this period (Moran, Proctor, Mueser, and Rutledge, 1959), including the first recorded slides at Castellammare Mesa in March 1933. Residential road construction north of PCH was started in 1925. An oblique air photograph dated December 6, 1925, documents the effects of recent grading. Streets were graded, and water mains and a sanitary sewer were installed. A promenade and stone-masonry wall were constructed near the toe of slope as part of the overall tract development.

Residential development

Many of the residences were constructed between 1927 and the early 1960s. The locations of residences constructed or significantly modified after 1969 are shown on Figure 5. The lots for the three homes on Porto Marina Way appear to have been graded sometime before 1958 (Maurseth, Howe, Lockwood, and Associates, 1967). The grading included a cut slope at the rear of the lots that subsequently failed. The failure damaged a sewer line that leaked, apparently for some time, at two separate locations.

Review of post-1963 geotechnical and geological reports for residential construction permits in the WCML area indicates a significant variation in geologic opinion regarding the existence, depth, and location of landslides. For example, several reports indicated the existence of a landslide under lots north of Porto Marina Way near Lecco Lane. Other reports indicated that the landslide did not exist. It is interesting to note that homes in this area were either partially or totally destroyed in 1993.

Rains and Landslides of the Early 1940s and 1969

The southern edge of Porto Marina Way failed during the winter rains of 1940–1941. Rainfall recorded at Los Angeles Civic Center was 83.2 cm (32.76 in). Most of the slope west of Lecco Lane and south of Porto Marina Way was involved in some type of movement or failure. Between February and April 1941, movement was suspected in all of the Castellammare slide areas (Moran, Proctor, Mueser, and Rutledge, 1959). It is probable during this period that a number of the local streets were significantly cracked and water mains and sewer lines were damaged and not properly repaired (Moran, Proctor, Mueser, and Rutledge, 1959).

The winter rains of 1968–1969 were relatively intense (69.8 cm or 27.47 in) recorded at Los Angeles Civic Center). It was during this period that the "modern" history of slope failures started, following enactment of the 1963 grading ordinances. In January 1969, city of Los Angeles personnel first noted cracking at 17900 Porto Marina Way and in the street (Fig. 1). By February 17, the residence reportedly started to fail

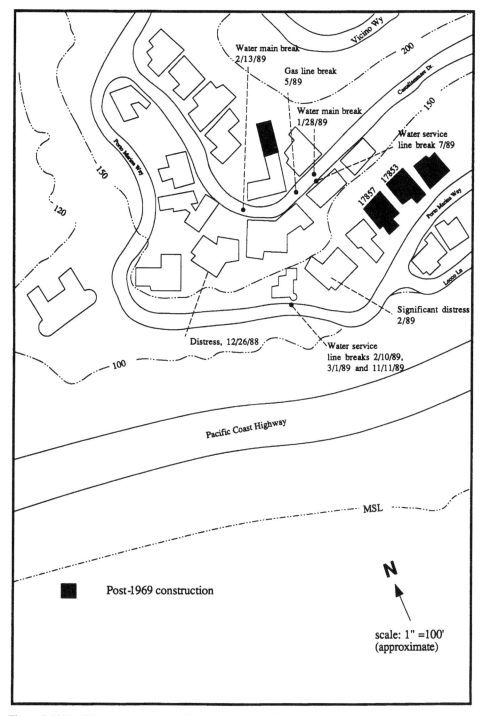

Figure 5. Utility failures and observed distress in the west Castellammare Mesa area of Pacific Palisades, late 1988 and 1989.

as it moved toward PCH. On February 20, the house was destroyed by the landslide. The base of the slide was reported to be about 6.1 m (20 ft) above PCH. On February 25, cracking was observed in the street between 17901 and 17908 Castellammare Drive and at 17909 Porto Marina Way. The maximum scarp height in Porto Marina Way was 3.66 m (12 ft) on April 12, 1969. The head scarps of these failures were mapped by the city of Los Angeles and are shown on Figure 1.

On November 27, 1969, continued slide movement resulted in the failure of the 15.24-cm (6-in) water main in the street in front of 17901 Castellammare Drive (Fig. 1). According to a memo from the Water Engineering Design Division, dated January 28, 1970, the line failed in tension with a 3.8-cm (1.5-in) separation. On November 28, 1969, adjustable mechanical couplings were installed to repair the leak. On December 10, the water service line connecting 17901 Castellammare Drive with the 15.24-cm (6-in) main line failed. Gravity flow sewer lines most likely also failed during this time. Sewer line leaks are generally more difficult to locate compared with water line failures and often go unnoticed.

As part of the review of the November water line failure the city of Los Angeles noted that "cracks sealed with tar appear to have reopened, mostly near H-17884 and H-17912. The incidence of cracking appears to have increased since early November." The city also stated: "The subject site may be undergoing adjustment to changes in stress, induced by the landslide at 17900 Porto Marina Way. The slope adjustment showed signs of evolving into an incipient landslide." A December 30, 1969, report presented the first reporting by the Bureau of Engineering that included data concerning waterline breaks on private property. This report stated: "Such breaks of waterlines on private property might be an indication of accelerated downhill movement and may provide additional water to preexisting hydrostatic forces."

Slope, street, and residential deterioration (1970 to 1993)

The first major city of Los Angeles street repairs since 1946 were initiated in 1970. Construction to support or rebuild Porto Marina Way and Castellammare Drive was underway by January 5, 1970. 18.29-m (60-ft)-long I-beams were installed along the 17900 block of Castellammare Drive (Fig. 1). A bulkhead was constructed along the south side of Porto Marina Way. Monitoring of potential future slope movement was also started with the installation of slope indicators at 17912 Castellammare Drive and across the street from 17919 Porto Marina Way. Movement was recorded at depths greater than 9.1 m (30 ft) in both SIs (City of Los Angeles, 1984).

The low shear strength of slope materials became evident in January 1972 when the city noted cracking at the top of the I-beams in front of 17908 Castellammare Drive. Dewatering wells were installed soon after the distress was observed. One of the wells in Castellammare Drive was dry or had little flow. The other, at 17912 Castellammare Drive, produced significant quantities of water for a number of years (City of Los Angeles, 1984). During the first week of November 1972, city of Los Angeles personnel also observed cracking in the street between 17901 and 17908 Castellammare Drive. A third SI was installed at 17908 Castellammare on March 16, 1973. Movement was recorded at 11.6 m (38 ft).

Significant cracking and distress were noted along Castellammare Drive and Porto Marina Way directly related to the heavy rains of 1977–1978 (Fig. 4) (84.9 cm or 33.44 in of rainfall recorded at Los Angeles Civic Center). Clear visual evidence of movement was observed between or around the caissons in the street in front of 17908 Castellammare Drive (Buckley and Hollingsworth, 1984). Slide material extruded between "the nominal 8-foot caisson spacing causing settlement of the street and a 1 to 3-inch hump of the street surface over the top of the caisson

locations" (City of Los Angeles, 1984). During March 1978, significant cracking developed in the street in front of 17909 and 17919 Porto Marina Way. In front and west of 17919 Porto Marina Way, I-beams and a bulkhead were constructed for street support. The Los Angeles, Department of Building and Safety gave approval, on November 29, 1978, to construct several residences along Porto Marina Way (Fig. 4). Within 5 yr, the western lots and residences exhibited signs of distress.

The 1977–1978 rains were followed by two consecutive winters of above-average rainfall, including 50 cm (19.67 in) during the winter of 1978–1979 and 68.5 cm (26.98 in) during the 1979–1980 rainfall season. As a result, in early 1980 the city of Los Angeles noted distress at the bulkhead below 17909 Porto Marina Way. Water was also observed flowing from the bulkhead. Because of the effects of the rains, the city of Los Angeles in late March 1980 installed a dewatering well 7.9 m (13 ft) east of the western lot line of 17908 Castellammare Drive. A few days later, on April 1, 1980, a second dewatering well was installed 0.9 m (3 ft) east of the west edge of the residence at 17884 Castellammare Drive. Odor from sewage was noted on the boring log for the second well.

Apparently as a result of the progressive failure of Porto Marina Way, the California Department of Transportation (Caltrans, 1980) noted the following on September 19, 1980: "The City of Los Angeles constructed soldier beam walls with timber lagging along the seaward side of Porto Marina Way in an attempt to prevent loss of the street. A section of the wall is beginning to fail and reinforcement will probably be required. . . . A cooperative effort between the City and State may be necessary to maintain the highway at this location" (p. 56).

On October 10, 1980, the homeowner at 17884 Castellammare Drive noted street settlement in front of the residence, and the tops of the I-beams were exposed, resulting in poor street drainage. The owner also complained that the dewatering wells, installed in the 1970s, were not automatic, and it was necessary for the homeowners to activate the pumps daily.

The 1980–1981 and the 1981–1982 winters had a combined rainfall of less than 50.8 cm (20 in). However, in late May 1981 the Department of Water and Power noted seepage at 17884 and 17908 Castellammare Drive. By mid-June of the same year there was clear evidence of distress at 17908 Castellammare Drive. In March 1982, the city noted shallow water, smelling like sewer water, in an SI casing between 17919 and 17945 Porto Marina Way. A city inspection of 17912 Castellammare Drive on May 28, 1982, indicated "house vacant—driveway cracked. . . ." The house was later sold and partially reconstructed.

The 1982–1983 rainfall season was a near record 79.4 cm (31.25 in) for the Los Angeles Civic Center (Slosson and Larson, 1995). In early 1983, the city's dewatering wells along Castellammare Drive were working. However, it is important to note that water pumped from the wells was placed in the street and allowed to flow east across the main scarp of the 1969 failure (Fig. 1) and distressed zones observed in 1978 and early 1983 (Fig. 4). As a result, in late April 1983 water from the wells was noted flowing eastward along Castellammare Drive, crossing the street near

17908, and infiltrating into a zone of ponding, cracking, and settlement at the southeast corner of the residence at 17901 Castellammare Drive (Fig. 4). The reported maximum discharge from the four wells was 121.13 L/min (32 gal/min). On August 3, 1983, the city noted pumped well water flowing into cracks around the I–beams in Castellammare Drive. As a result of slide movement in September 1983, the sewer service line to 17901 Castellammare Drive had to be lengthened 15.24 to 20.32 cm (6 to 8 in) to maintain the connection between the house and the main line in the street.

Continued slope movement resulted in the rupture of the water main between 17901 and 17884 Castellammare Drive on October 15, 1983 (Fig. 4). The following was noted on a city of Los Angeles Geologic Field Data Sheet dated October 17, 1983: "The leak had been repaired and the street patched on October 15, 1983. Water from the leak appeared to have run easterly along the south curb where some portion of the flow overtopped the curb in front of H-17884 and ran along the front footing wall of the house. . . . The pavement showed evidence of settlement, especially around the tops of several soldier beams next to the south curb in front of H-17884 and H-17908. The house at 17912, which has been under reconstruction for several months, showed evidence of additional settlement along the front wall." Following the October break, the city considered the feasibility of placing the water main in Castellammare Drive on the surface to allow for early leak detection and then made weekly inspections of the Castellammare area for signs of new or continued slope movement. The water line was not placed at the surface until after a series of breaks in early 1989. During the drought years of the mid-1980s, movement within the WCML slowed but appears never to have stopped.

The 15.2-cm (6-in) water main in front of 17884 Castellammare Drive broke again on January 28, 1989, 10 days after an offshore, magnitude 5 earthquake (Fig. 5). The break occurred at or near the location of the 1983 break and east of the 1969 failure. Water from the failure accelerated slide movement. Thirteen days later the service water line broke at 17919 Porto Marina Way. Flow lasted 54 hr before repair. The city considered the leak too minor to repair on an emergency basis. Significant settlement and down slope movement were noted next door at 17909 Porto Marina Way. On February 13, 1989, a second tensional break in the 15.2-cm (6-in) water main occurred in the street near 17901 Castellammare Drive (Fig. 5). Damage was observed along the down slope side of the street at 17908 and 17912 Castellammare Drive. By the end of June 1989 the bulkhead along the south side of Porto Marina Way showed new distress, new cracks were observed at 17909 Porto Marina Way and 17908 Castellammare Drive, and settlement was noted at 17884 Castellammare Drive.

In December 1989 the city again recommended that the water mains and services lines be placed above ground for easy leak detection. Also in December, a geologic review of 17909 Porto Marina Way indicated significant distress to the residence and surrounding property (Solus Geotechnical, 1990). In a follow-up review in early 1990, compressional features were observed, indicating that the rear slope was moving toward the residence.

On May 11, 1990, the city recommended the placement of barricades in front of 17908 Castellammare Drive because of settlement and surface cracking. In January 1991 a manometer survey was conducted at 17919 Porto Marina Way (Robertson Geotechnical, Inc., 1991). The survey indicated that the residence had tilted. Compressional features were also observed in the garage area. In April 1992, I noted ponding between the residences at 17901 and 17885 Castellammare Drive (Fig. 4) and cracking in the street. By early October cracking was also observed in Porto Marina Way near 17909.

The rains of 1993

At the start of the 1992–1993 rains, Castellammare Drive and Porto Marina Way were distressed. Street cracks were common, and ponding was a problem along Castellammare Drive. The bulkhead on Porto Marina Way and the street around the I-beams on Castellammare Drive were also distressed. Surface flow along the streets was infiltrating into the WCML at the main scarp (Figs. 1 and 4) and lower portions of the slide along Porto Marina Way. The stage was set for the catastrophic failures of 1993.

During the early morning hours of January 18, 1993, I observed the following distress along Castellammare Drive and Porto Marina Way:

1. The gas line in the street near the southwest corner of 17901 Castellammare Drive had broken.

2. Surface water was flowing into street cracks between 17901 and 17912 Castellammare Drive (Fig. 6) and at the southwest corner of 17885 Castellammare Drive (I could hear the flow of water into and along cracks and voids below the street as well as gas bubbling up through the flowing water).

3. The water main failed in the street southwest of the residence at 17945 Porto Marina near a zone of cracking observed in 1983 (Figs. 4 and 7).

4. Surface flow along Porto Marina Way and flow from the broken water main were entering a series of shear and tension

Figure 6. View of tension crack near the southwest edge of 17901 Castellammare Drive. Note the flow of surface water into the fracture and the aboveground water line. The photograph was taken on the morning of January 18, 1993.

Figure 7. View looking east along Porto Marina Way near the southwest corner of 17945 Porto Marina Way. Note, in the foreground, flow of muddy water from a broken water main in the center of the street. The photograph was taken on the morning of January 18, 1993.

cracks in Porto Marina Way as far east as the western intersection of Porto Marina Way and Lecco Lane.

5. The slope below Porto Marina and west of Lecco Lane had failed at several locations (Fig. 8).

Forty-eight hours later, on January 20, 1993, I observed additional movement and cracking in the floor of the garage at 17885 Castellammare Drive. Cracking extended west of the garage onto the property at 17901 Castellammare Drive. Although less clear at the time, evidence of additional movement was noted in the stairs along the eastern side of the residence. Castellammare Drive between 17885 and 17912 had dropped ~0.3 m (1 ft). Significant additional distress was noted in the bulkhead below 17909 Porto Marina Way. Extensional and shear cracking was observed in the street above the wall along its entire length from Lecco Lane westward (Fig. 9). The tension gashes shown on Fig. 9 were the direct result of the forma-

Figure 9. View due south of 17909 Porto Marina Way. Note tension gashes in the street. Photograph taken April 13, 1993.

tion of a right lateral shear zone in Porto Marina Way. Additional cracking was noted in the street and top of slope south and west of 17919 Porto Marina Way.

On January 22, 1993, a temporary, aboveground sewer line was placed along the street between 17945 and 17909 Porto Marina Way (Fig. 8). An aboveground water line was installed on Porto Marina Way, and flexible service lines were installed on Porto Marina Way and Castellammare Drive. On February 24, 1993, I observed the rear yard of the residence at 17863 Porto Marina Way. The retaining wall at the rear of the yard was distressed as was the brick planter along the base of the wall. Two large trees were leaning to the south upslope of the wall. Significant cracking existed in the patio between the wall and the house, in the wall along the western edge of the property, and in the public walkway along the western side of the residence. The slope above the residence, including the house at 17884 Castellammare Drive, was sliding toward the rear yard. Asphalt in the street in front of the garage was locally overriding asphalt, indicating compression at that location. The sidewalk east of the garage was tilted to the north. I noted cracking in the street as far east as 17853 Porto Marina Way. Cracks also had developed at the southwest corner of the residence at 17853. Cracks at that location were opening at the approximate rate of 0.13 cm (0.05 in) per day in late February. A significant scarp had developed across the residence at 17912 Castellam-

Figure 8. View northwest along Porto Marina Way west of 17919. Note landslide toward PCH, I-beams exposed next to the street, and the aboveground sewer line. Sand bags were placed by the city of Los Angeles to control surface flow and infiltration. The photograph was taken on February 24, 1993.

Figure 10. View southwest toward 17912 Castellammare Drive. The failure zone is the main scarp of Q_{als}-3 as shown on Figure 12. The photograph was taken on August 12, 1993.

Figure 11. View west along Castellammare Drive in front of 17908. Note I-beams visible along the curb and plastic and sand bags placed by the city of Los Angeles. The photograph was taken on February 24, 1993.

mare Drive (Fig. 10), and the street had dropped in front of 17908, exposing the top of the I-beams placed in 1969 (Fig. 11).

By the end of February the pattern of cracking and distress along Castellammare Drive and Porto Marina Way was, in many ways, similar to that noted in 1969, 1978, and 1983. However, the zone of distress was clearly larger than had been mapped before (Fig. 12).

In early March the compression noted in the street at 17863 Porto Marina Way was visible as a linear zone in the street parallel to the sidewalk and extending a few meters east of the garage at 17857 (Fig. 12). By late March the city installed dewatering wells in Castellammare Drive as part of their proposed street repairs. However, by April 1, the wells were failing at ~9.8 m (32 ft) below existing street grade (Fig. 13). The city shut down the wells on April 9, 1993. Soon after that date, construction began on repair of Castellammare Drive with the installation of 24.4-m (80-ft) I-beams along Castellammare Drive. Figure 14 is a view looking northwest across the WCML from the eastern end of Porto Marina Way. The top of the drill rig and the crane placing the I-beams are visible in the background on Castellammare Drive. The distressed residence below the crane is located at 17908 Castellammare Drive. Note the construction of a new residence in the foreground along the south side of Lecco Lane. The extent of the construction along Porto Marina Way, northwest of

17909 Porto Marina Way, as of the first week in September 1993 is shown in Figure 15.

The regional pattern of surface cracking, local distress, and the patchwork of repairs evolved between 1969 and late 1992 as noted above. However, the extensive and clear pattern of distress shown on Figure 12 developed rapidly following the heavy rains of January 18, 1993. Evidence of slope movement within the complex rock slide was observed as far north as the rear patio area of 17885 Castellammare Drive and as far south as the slope above PCH. The crown of the active slide is ~56.4 to 57.9 m (185 to 190 ft) above sea level. The toe of the slide is at an elevation of ~12.2 m 40 ft). As of early May 1993, the eastern edge of the slide complex could be traced to cracking in the street in front of and between 17847 and 17853 Porto Marina Way. The western edge of the slide, at that time, affected the drive (to the garage) in front of 17948 Porto Marina Way. Nearly the entire slope between Porto Marina Way and PCH had failed and was moving slowly.

Boundaries of individual slides were mapped by tracing on foot the limits of the failure across public streets and private property. The existence of the main slide and each secondary landslide was based on the ability to map a general pattern of tensional features (grabens) near the main scarp (Fig. 6), shear cracking (Fig. 7) and tension gashes (Fig. 9) along the edges, and zones of compression or shortening at the toe. The 1993 pattern of cracking and distress was similar to that noted in 1969 and 1983. However, there is evidence to suggest that the limits of the current episode of accelerated movement have exceeded that noted or mapped by others (Figs. 1, 4, and 12). The outer limits of the pattern of cracking nearly correspond to the air photograph landslide interpretation shown on Figure 12. Comparison of 1993 pattern of failures with the air photointerpretation shown on Figure 12 suggests the active slide area could enlarge to the north and east and that additional failures are possible to the northwest.

Surface mapping clearly indicates that a number of secondary slope failures are occurring within a larger and somewhat deeper

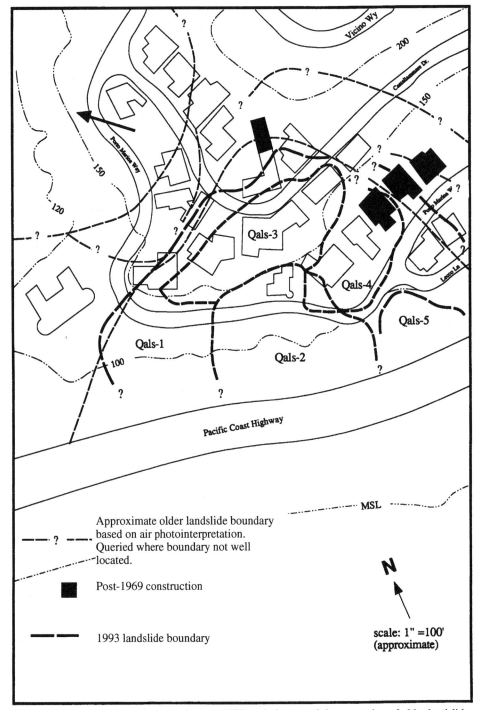

Figure 12. Slope failures activated in January 1993, and photograph interpretation of older landslides.

active landslide (Q_{als}-1). Offset and distressed cultural features such as streets, houses, and walk ways suggest the deep landslide, Q_{als}-1, is moving nearly due south or slightly southeast. The shallower, secondary landslides, Q_{als}-2 to Q_{als}-5, appear to be failing in direct response to local topography. For example, secondary failures mapped west of Lecco Lane and generally south of the upslope edge of Porto Marina Way are moving southwestward,

perpendicular to contours above PCH (Fig. 12). The toe or base of a relatively shallow failure is exposed above Porto Marina Way at the rear of residences including and between 17857 and 17919 Porto Marina Way (Q_{als}-3). A similar, although apparently deeper, failure toes up in the street in front of the residences at 17857, 17863, and 17909 Porto Marina Way (Q_{als}-4).

The northern limit of the WCML, as of June 15, 1993,

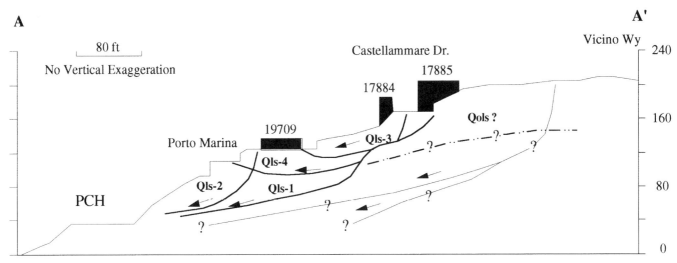

Figure 13. Geologic cross section A-A'. Heavy solid lines denote surface of rupture of landslides reactivated in 1993 (Q_{ls}-1, etc.); thin solid lines denote surface rupture of an older landslide (Q_{ols}); double dot and dashed line denotes estimated perched water based on subsurface data. Q_{ols} surface of rupture based on air photointerpretation and review of deep boring data. Location of the profile indicated in Figure 12.

Figure 14. View west, above PCH, looking across the 1993 landslide(s). The crane and drill rig, in the background, are on Castellammare Drive. Note the new house under construction. The photograph was taken on April 16, 1993.

Figure 15. View west along Porto Marina Way taken due south of the drive at 17909 , Marina Way. The photograph was taken on October 11, 1993, at a location several tens of meters southeast of that in Figure 8.

extended eastward from 17916 Castellammare Drive to the eastern end of 17884 Castellammare Drive, crossing the southern portion of the residence at 17901 Castellammare Drive (Fig. 12) at an approximate elevation of 52 m (170 ft) above sea level. Clear evidence of the northern extent of the slide was also observed at 17885 Castellammare Drive. Tension cracking north of the main scarp suggests that the slope or crown in this region is unstable. Tension and shear cracks along Castellammare Drive were mapped in the street on the northwest side of 17912, across the residence at 17901 in an eastward direction, then easterly across 17885 to the northeastern corner of the res-

idence at 17884. The active slide boundary at that point appears to turn southward.

A zone of cracking and distress on the slope between Castellammare Drive and Porto Marina Way marks the location of an active landslide (Q_{als}-3) that daylights above Porto Marina Way (Fig. 12). A well-defined failure plane was exposed near the toe in a small excavation along the western wall of the residence at 17919 Porto Marina Way. The compression zone at the toe of Q_{als}-3 trends eastward along the drive and rear yard of the residence at 17909 Porto Marina Way and the public walk along the west side of 17863 Porto Marina Way. The westerly and north walls at the rear of 17863 Porto Marina Way were significantly distressed. The existence of compressional features indicates that Q_{als}-3 is moving faster than the "host" failure (e.g., Cronin, 1992), Q_{als}-1. For example, the residence at 17884 Castellammare Drive has dropped vertically 1.22 to 1.5 m (4 to 5 ft) below street grade, whereas residences below, along the north side of Porto Marina Way, are in compression. A second zone of compression was observed in the street in front of 17857, 17863, and 17909 Porto Marina Way (Q_{als}-4). The western extent of the zone of compression, observed in Porto Marina Way, was terminated or cut off by relatively rapid movement of another secondary landslide that is affecting the residences at 17909 and 17919 Porto Marina Way (Q_{als}-2). The result is that various portions of the property at 17909 Porto Marina Way are either in compression or are undergoing a combination of shear and tension cracking.

Landslide repairs were underway in April 1993 (Fig. 14). The city of Los Angeles started construction near the main scarp (Fig. 12) and then moved down slope along Porto Marina Way (Fig. 15). By December 1993, most of the construction for support

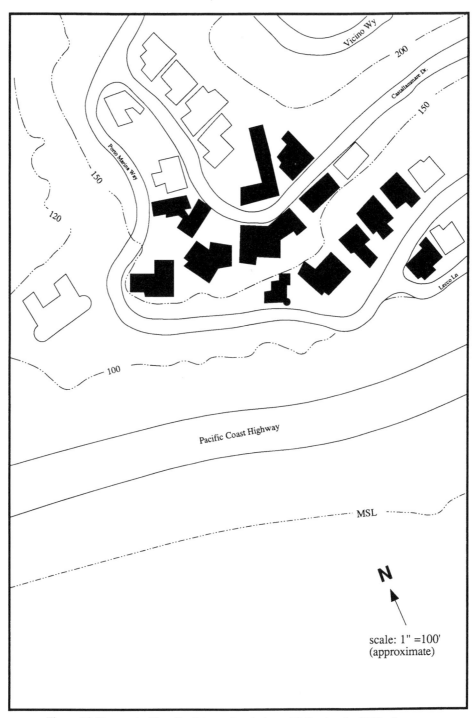

Figure 16. Homes significantly distressed or destroyed following the 1993 rains.

of Castellammare Drive and Porto Marina Way had been completed. The residences at 17884, 17908, and 17912 Castellammare Drive had been removed and the lots were graded. The slope below Porto Marina Way had also been regraded. The grading was surficial, designed only to improve the appearance of the area. The locations of residences that to my knowledge were destroyed or significantly distressed as of late 1993 are shown in Figure 16. Other structures near the mapped boundary of the WCML may also have been affected. However, direct evidence was not available at the time. The WCML, as shown on Figures 12 and 13, is approximately 152 m (500 ft) long by 91 m (300 ft) wide, and its surface of rupture is ~18+ m (60+ ft) below Porto Marina Way. The WCML also appears to be smaller than the series of failures interpreted from air photographs, which suggests that intervention by the city of Los Angeles may have kept the landslide from enlarging to prehistoric dimensions.

In February 1995, cracking was observed in the recently paved street, suggesting slope movement along the west side of 17945 Porto Marina Way. Water was seeping, uncontrolled, at several locations along the base of the bulkhead below 17909 Porto Marina Way. The slope below Porto Marina Way was distressed, locally failing onto PCH, and water was once again being pumped to the street and allowed to flow at the surface, eastward across the head scarp along Castellammare Drive.

CONCLUSIONS

Significant conclusions are:

1. The WCML is a relatively large, reactivated, complex rock slide or multiple slide system that includes a relatively large "host" landslide (Q_{als}-1) and at least four major, active, secondary landslides. It is underlain by an apparently deeper landslide(s) that does not appear to have been active since development in the 1920s. The system of landslides, both active and inactive, is larger and more complex than that mapped by either McGill (1982a, 1989) or Dibblee (1992). The secondary landslides moved at different rates, affected by somewhat different geologic, topographic, cultural, and/or groundwater conditions.

2. Existing data indicate that the most recent episode of accelerated movement within the WCML started on the morning of January 18, 1993. The relatively rapid movement observed that morning was exacerbated by the cumulative effects of a series of events, including significant rainfall, failure of the water main on Porto Marina Way, surface flow of water into pre-existing street cracks, ponding and infiltration along Castellammare Drive, and an ineffective dewatering program.

3. High rainfall seasons, such as 1992–1993, clearly demonstrate the need for detailed regional geological and geotechnical studies before lot by lot construction can reasonably proceed. Studies should be reviewed by a single governmental agency or department with the technical expertise and responsibility needed to coordinate the studies and implement regional and lot by lot private, public utility, and governmental mitigation efforts. Mitigation of existing and potential future slope failures will require

the integrated efforts of government officials and locally affected property owners. Slosson and Larson (1995) list a number of reasons why landslides damage and/or destroy public and private property during periods of high rainfall. Our respective conclusions are consistent as to the effects of periods of high rainfall and related human causes.

4. Regional mitigation objectives should include a major reduction in the infiltration of surface water into the slope above PCH and the permanent maintenance of a relatively low pressure or potentiometric surface. Review of the historic behavior of slopes in the area, since construction of the first street support system in the early 1970s, indicates that the city's existing improvements to Castellammare Drive and Porto Marina Way may not be enough to mitigate future slope movement without the installation of an effective regional dewatering system. Mitigation efforts should include the long-term protection of all water lines, sewer mains, and storm drains within and above the slide area. Both main lines and residential service connections will require protection from rupture. Slope materials are too weak to be contained by the recently constructed support system if they are moist or saturated.

ACKNOWLEDGMENTS

I would like to thank the anonymous and noted reviewers for the helpful comments and suggestions. I would also like to thank Robert Larson and Jim Slosson for their time, assistance, and patience.

REFERENCES CITED

Buckley, C., and Hollingsworth, R. A., 1984, Residential development and landsliding, Castellammare Mesa area, Los Angeles, California, *in* Association of Engineering Geologists Field Trip Guidebook, Engineering geologic features, Malibu, Los Angeles County, California, June 2, 1984: p. 54–63.

Caltrans, 1980, Landslide inventory, Pacific Coast Highway, McClure Tunnel to Las Flores Canyon road, 07-LA-1, P.M.35.17/44.12, District 7, Materials Section, 85 p.

City of Los Angeles, 1984, Geology and soils engineering report, Claim of H. Warcharzer and M. Rosen, 17901 Castellamare Dr., signed by G. Stolt, July 23.

Cronin, V. S., 1992, Compound landslides: Nature and hazard potential of secondary landslides within host landslides, *in* Slosson, J. E., Keene, A. G., and Johnson, J. A., eds., Landslides/landslide mitigation: Geological Society of America Reviews in Engineering Geology, v. 9, p. 1–9.

Dibblee, T. W., 1992, Geologic map of the Topanga and Canoga Park (South 1/2) Quadrangles, Los Angeles County, California: Dibblee Geological Foundation, scale 1:24000.

Geology and Soils Consultants, Inc., 1972, Addendum report, engineering geologic and soils engineering investigation, lots 3 and 4, Castellammare Tract, Lecco Lane, Pacific Palisades, California, GSC job no. 160, July 24, 10 p.

Hoots, R. W., 1930, Geology of the eastern part of the Santa Monica Mountains, LA Co., California, U.S. Geological Survey Professional Paper 165c, 178 p.

Jeffrey A. Johnson, Inc., 1993, Preliminary geologic exploration, West Castellammare Mesa landslide; Proposed remedial repairs, distressed residences, 17909 and 17919 Porto Marino Way, Pacific Palisades, CA: Service No. 93-01-5000, June 10, 28 p.

Maurseth, Howe, Lockwood, and Associates, 1967, Report of a foundation and geologic investigation, lots 24, 25 and 26, block 3, M.B. 113, pages 4–6, located at 17849 to 17857 Porto Marina Way, Los Angeles, California, Project No. 4009-FG, March 22, 7 p.

McGill, J. T., 1982a, Preliminary geologic map of the Pacific Palisades area, City of Los Angeles, California: U.S. Geological Survey Open-File Report, 82-194, scale 1:4,800.

McGill, J. T., 1982b, Map showing relationship of historic to prehistoric landslides, Pacific Palisades area, City of Los Angeles, California: U.S. Geological Survey Miscellaneous Field Studies Map MF-1455, scale 1:4,800.

McGill, J. T., 1989, Geologic maps of the Pacific Palisades area, City of Los Angeles, California: U.S. Geological Survey Miscellaneous Investigations Map I-1828, scale 1:4,800.

Moran, Proctor, Mueser, and Rutledge, 1959, Final report, Pacific Palisades landslide study, Volume 1, 68 p.; Volume 2, 45 p.; Volume 3, 46 p., July.

Prevost, D. V., 1993, Development of the Castellammare Mesa Landslide Area, *in*

Engineering geology field trips Orange County, Santa Monica and Malibu: Association of Engineering Geologists 35th Annual Meeting, Long Beach, California, Oct. 2–9, p. B-102.

Robertson Geotechnical, Inc., 1991, Report on preliminary engineering geologic evaluation, proposed repair of existing residence, 17919 Porto Marina Way, Pacific Palisades, California, 1554LELA.115, January 18.

Slosson, J. E., and Larson, R. A., 1995, Slope failures in Southern California: Rainfall threshold, prediction and human causes: Environmental and Engineering Geoscience, v. 1, Winter, p. 393–401.

Solus Geotechnical, 1990, Geotechnical engineering evaluation for remedial repair of existing distressed residence, lot 8, Castle Rock tr., 17909 Porto Marina Way, Pacific Palisades area, City of Los Angeles, California, work order #89164, February 5.

Manuscript Accepted by the Society January 29, 1997

Geological Society of America
Reviews in Engineering Geology, Volume XI
1997

La Ventana landslide, cities of San Clemente and Dana Point, California

William Goodman
NMG Geotechnical, Inc., 17791 Mitchell, Suite D, Irvine, California 92714
Jules Darras
Zeiser Kling Consultants, Inc., 3187 Redhill Avenue, Suite 135, Costa Mesa, California 92626

ABSTRACT

A block-glide debris-fall landslide occurred on February 22, 1993, within a 30.5-m (100-ft)-high bluff in the Capistrano Beach area in the cities of Dana Point and San Clemente, Orange County, California. Five homes were destroyed, and several others remained in jeopardy subsequent to this catastrophic ground failure. The landslide caused the bluff top to retreat a maximum of 24.4 m (80 ft) and deposited 20,000 m³ (27,000 cy³) of landslide debris up to 10.5 m (35 ft) deep on Pacific Coast Highway (PCH), a designated emergency evacuation route for the San Onofre nuclear-powered electricity generating station. The landslide debris also covered a 76.2-m (250-ft) section of the only rail line linking the Los Angeles/Orange County area with San Diego.

The winter storms preceding this landslide brought 53.3 cm (21 in) of rain to the Capistrano Beach area. The single-month peak of 29 cm (11.44 in) occurred in January and was the highest in 30 yr. This excessive rainfall infiltrated the subsurface, triggering the landslide, which failed on an adverse-dipping clay bed at approximately midslope of the 30.5-m (100-ft)-high bluffs. The landslide scarp was controlled by high-angle bedrock jointing.

Mitigation alternatives were restrictive because of the many public/private landowners involved and the fact that the city boundary between Dana Point and San Clemente is located in the upper part of the bluff. Initially, the various stabilization options considered to reopen PCH were restricted within the jurisdiction of Dana Point. Eventually, the failed portion of the bluff was restored by a system of rock-bolt tiebacks combined with a hardface wall and buttressed slope. Subdrainage was installed along the buttress backcut and behind the hardface wall, and outlets were provided at the slope face.

INTRODUCTION

The winter rains of 1992–1993 had a significant impact on the coastal bluffs in the Capistrano Beach area of Dana Point–San Clemente, Orange County, California. Although the cumulative rainfall total for the year was not extraordinarily high, the single-month rainfall in January was the highest in 30 yr. At about 10:45 P.M. on February 22, 1993, a large part of the coastal bluff failed, destroying five homes and inundating Pacific Coast Highway (PCH), the Atchison, Topeka, and Santa Fe Railroad, and a part of Beach Road.

The La Ventana landslide is located northwest of the intersection of PCH and Camino Capistrano in the cities of Dana Point and San Clemente, California (Fig. 1). La Ventana Street runs parallel to PCH at the top of the bluff for ~377 m (1,270± ft). The relief from the top of the bluff to PCH is ~30.5 m (100± ft) in a

Goodman, W., and Darras, J., 1997, La Ventana landslide, cities of San Clemente and Dana Point, California, *in* Larson, R. A., and Slosson, J. E., eds., Storm-Induced Geologic Hazards: Case Histories from the 1992–1993 Winter in Southern California and Arizona: Boulder, Colorado, Geological Society of America Reviews in Engineering Geology, v. XI.

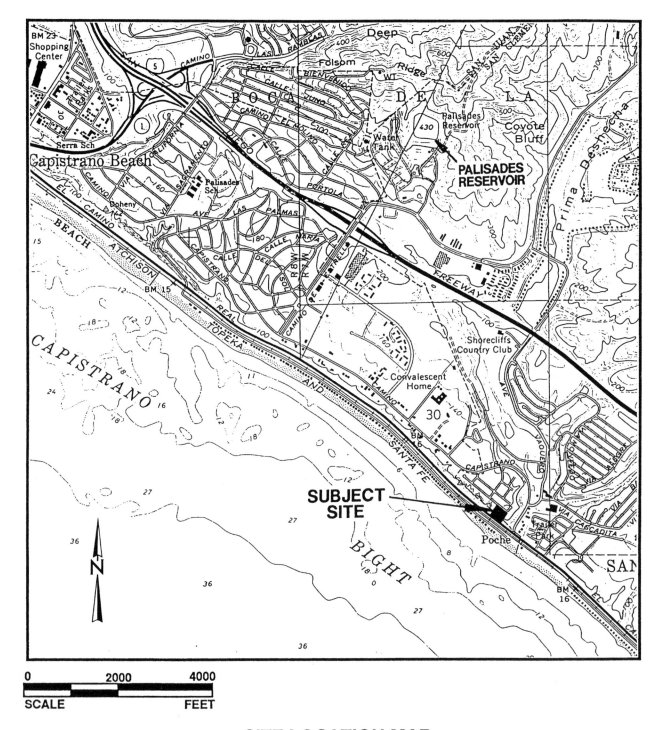

SITE LOCATION MAP

Figure 1. Map showing location of La Ventana landslide. Modified from U.S. Geological Survey
Dana Point 7.5-Minute Quadrangle.

horizontal span ranging from 24 to 37 m (80 to 120± ft). The
Atchison, Topeka, and Santa Fe Railroad is located ~15.2 m
(50 ft) southwest of PCH.

The upper part of the bluff in the Palisades area is typically
rounded and has moderate slope angles (20 to 25°) as a result of

erosion of the granular terrace deposits exposed there. Well-bedded
and jointed siltstone bedrock with essentially flat-lying bedding is
exposed in the mid-portion of the bluff. This portion of the bluff is
very steep (60 to 70°) and locally vertical to overhanging. Massive
siltstone crops out below the well-bedded unit. The lower portion of

the bluff is mostly covered with talus deposits, which results in slope angles of 30 to 35°.

PREVIOUS GEOLOGIC STUDIES

The subject site lies within the Dana Point Quadrangle. The California Division of Mines and Geology (CDMG) completed a geologic study of this quadrangle in 1974 (Edgington, 1974). The geologic map accompanying that report shows the La Ventana site to be underlain by the Capistrano Formation, with a thin veneer (6 m [20 ft]) of artificial fill and nonmarine terrace deposits capping the bluff-top area. The orientation of the strata of this sedimentary formation was depicted as generally flat lying. In that report, Edgington discussed the accelerated rate of bluff failure from San Juan Creek to San Clemente "due to increased seepage from heavy periodic rainfall and irrigation of yards in the urbanizing areas inland" (p. 4).

An engineering geologic report on the Capistrano Beach area was published by R and M Consultants, Inc., in May 1982. The purpose of the report was to provide input for the Capistrano Beach specific plan and was included as a technical appendix to the environmental impact report for the specific plan. The geologic map accompanying that report shows similar contacts for the geologic units as depicted in Edgington (1974). However, in the vicinity of the La Ventana site, bedding was shown on the bluff face dipping 6 to 7° to the northwest, obliquely out-of-slope. This was the first report to document out-of-slope bedding at the site.

Zeiser Geotechnical completed an investigation of geotechnical conditions and historical erosion for the city of Dana Point coastal zone in July 1990. The geologic conditions shown on their accompanying geotechnical map in the vicinity of the site are similar to those on the map in R and M Consultants, Inc. (1982) (i.e., bedding dipping 6 to 7° northwest, obliquely out-of-slope). In addition, the Zeiser Geotechnical report showed a recent landslide on the bluff northwest of the La Ventana landslide site. The area was reported to have a very high risk for bluff instability and bluff-top erosion. Problematic seepage in the bluff area was mentioned as a contributing factor for historic bluff-top erosion and, to some degree, block-fall landsliding typical in this area.

In January 1993, Zeiser Kling Consultants, Inc. (1993a), evaluated a bluff failure northwest of the La Ventana site, ~122 to 183 m (400 to 600 ft) north of the intersection of PCH and Camino Capistrano. A portion of the rear yards (including patio improvements) for two homes on the west side of La Ventana Street were damaged. The purpose of the Zeiser Kling study was to provide the city of Dana Point with geotechnical recommendations for reopening PCH without endangering the affected residences at the top of the bluff adjacent to La Ventana Street. The slide mass consisted of saturated debris from the terrace deposits and some large blocky fragments of Capistrano siltstone. The basal rupture surface of this slide was reported to be on a previously existing shear separating the upper and lower siltstone units within the Capistrano Formation. Zeiser Kling concluded that water from the recent heavy rains combined with irrigation practices at the top of the

bluff and other possible water sources contributed to the mid-January landslide.

GENERAL BLUFF HISTORY

The bluffs in the Capistrano Beach area were originally situated along the beach. The primary agents causing retreat of the bluff prior to urbanization were rodent activity within the terrace cap, wave action cutting away the toe of slope, gravity acting on the weathered bluff face, and groundwater (essentially recharged by rain). During the 1880s, the bluff was cut back to provide access for the Atchison, Topeka, and Santa Fe Railroad, which now provides access for Amtrak between Orange County and San Diego. In 1929, with little regard for long-term stability, the bluff was again cut back (Fig. 2) to provide access for PCH (Walker, 1989). The construction, probably typical for the time, included a narrow setback at the road grade for accumulation of talus.

Stereographic vertical aerial photographs taken in July 1938 indicate that the site was undeveloped and covered with native grasses and chaparral-type shrubs. Erosional gullies visible in the vicinity of the future La Ventana landslide appear to have a shape similar to that shown on a predevelopment grading plan with a topographic base map (Ayer, 1960). The original lot numbers recorded in 1960 are depicted on the February 1993 postslide topographic base map (Fig. 3). The bluff top appears to have had a fairly uniform and steep profile in the vicinity of the site adjacent to PCH. Aerial photographs taken in 1952 indicate similar conditions.

In 1960, the area was graded for residential development (Ayer, 1960). Cutting and filling were performed to establish the design grades for the development, and the previously mentioned gullies were filled. The distance between the rear of the lots and the bluff face ranged from ~7.5 to 20 m (25 to 65 ft). By 1968, residences were constructed on all of the lots along the top of the bluff.

Figure 2. Photograph illustrating cutting of slopes adjacent to Pacific Coast Highway and Atchison, Topeka, and Santa Fe tracks in 1929. The exact location of the area in this photograph in uncertain, but it is believed to be in the vicinity of the intersection of Camino Capistrano and PCH. (Photograph courtesy of Doris Walker Collection.)

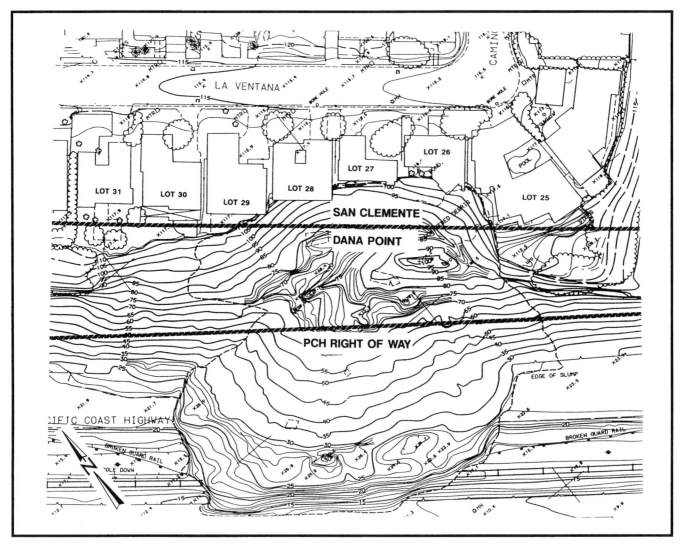

Figure 3. February 1993 base map illustrating location of municipal boundaries. The area between the PCH right-of-way and the Dana Point–San Clemente boundary is a parcel jointly owned by a consortium of individuals. Lot numbers indicated are from the grading plan (Ayer, 1960).

The first evidence of recent bluff failures at the site appear on oblique aerial photographs taken in 1973. It is likely that the majority of the fresh failures documented in these photographs had occurred in the above-average winter rainfall of 1969 (Fig. 4). An oblique aerial photograph (Fig. 5) taken in June 1979 shows fairly fresh failure scarps at the rear of Lots 25/26 and 29 through 31 (Fig. 3). This was after another year of above-average rainfall (Fig. 4) that caused damage in 1978. More important, Figure 5 shows three levels of linear seeps on the bluff face. One is at the base of the unconformable contact between the terrace deposits and the underlying siltstone of the Capistrano Formation. This seepage zone is relatively level, highlighting the position of the contact at the bluff face. The second seepage zone was at the base of the laminated, diatomaceous siltstone unit. This seepage extended diagonally across the bluff face from just below the terrace-bedrock contact behind Lot 26 to just below the mid-slope area behind

Lot 31. This seepage highlights bedding dipping west, oblique to the bluff face. A third seepage zone also highlighting bedding was present just below mid-slope on Lots 25 through 28. The angle of this seepage line was similar to that at the base of the laminated siltstone and is stratigraphically 12 m (40 ft) lower than the second seepage zone.

The second bluff failure to affect the site is depicted on a 1989 photograph (Fig. 6) and on a topographic base map (Rattray and Associates, Inc. 1990). This landslide damaged rear-yard improvements at Lots 29 and 30 but did not cause damage to the dwellings. Based on comparison of the 1960 topographic map (Ayer, 1960) to the 1990 topographic map (Rattray and Associates, Inc. 1990), the bluff adjacent to La Ventana Street had receded ~3 to 9 m (10 to 30 ft) as a result of erosion and episodic slope failures during that 30-year time period.

In mid-January 1993, a third episode of landsliding occurred

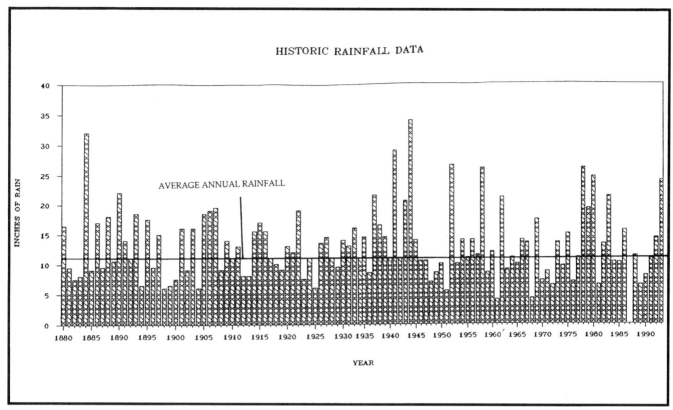

Figure 4. Historical rainfall data from gauging station at Irvine Ranch, California.

behind Lots 28 through 31, further damaging patio improvements at the rear of Lots 29 and 30 (Fig. 7). Approximately 4.6 m (15 ft) of bluff-top retreat occurred as a result of this slope failure, and debris covered PCH to a depth of up to ~1 m (3 ft), closing the road. The majority of the slide debris was saturated granular soils from the terrace deposits. Landslide activity continued in this area from mid-January until the major landslide of February 22, 1993. Cracks formed in and around the bluff-top residences between the mid-January failure and the main failure.

About one week prior to the February 22 landslide, the owner of Lot 27 found a crack in the interior floor slab of the house. The crack extended across the interior of the house parallel to the bluff face. Approximately 1.25 to 2.5 cm (0.5 to 1 in) of near-vertical separation was measured by the owner, west side down. Four days before the February 22 slide, the homeowner's geotechnical consultant recommended and performed pressure grouting to raise the dropped portion of the slab to its former elevation. Two days later, the slab had dropped down again with ~2.5 cm (1 in) of additional vertical separation. The homeowner, in an attempt to relieve structural stress, cut his house in half with a chain saw the day prior to the main landslide movement. The geologist representing the city of Dana Point recognized the evidence of incipient landslide movement and provided advance warning to the city of Dana Point prior to the failure.

Finally, at approximately 10:45 P.M. on February 22, 1993, the largest of the landslides in this area (informally referred to as

the La Ventana landslide) occurred within and behind Lots 25 through 30 (Figs. 3 and 8). This landslide caused an additional 18.3 to 24.4 m (60 to 80 ft) of bluff-top retreat and catastrophically damaged five homes on the west side of La Ventana Street. The Atchison, Topeka, and Santa Fe Railroad, PCH, and a part of Beach Road were covered by the landslide debris. A 91.5-m (300-ft) section of PCH remained buried by debris up to 11 m (35 ft) thick until clean-up activity began in August 1994. Construction of a temporary soldier-pile wall and subsequent removal of debris enabled the railroad to resume service within two weeks of the date of the landslide (Fig. 9).

STORM HISTORY

Historic rainfall data have been recorded in the southern California area since 1880 (Fig. 4), and additional qualitative data date back to as early as 1830. In his book *Two Years Before the Mast*, Richard Henry Dana provided accounts of violent storms along the California coast that were described by some ship's officers as similar to the storms often encountered at Cape Horn (Kuhn and Shepard, 1984). Dana described "Great Winds" from the south associated with heavy rain and very large ocean swells during the period from November to April. Dana also described 15- to 18-m (50- to 60-ft)-high waves with southeast winds, conditions that are extremely rare in the area today. Subtropical fish species were observed in coastal southern California waters dur-

Figure 5. Oblique aerial photograph taken in June 1979 after a winter with above-average rains. Note seepage at base of terrace sands and along bedding extending diagonally across the bluff face. Note arcuate scarps beneath first and fifth houses from right. (Copyright Geo Tech Imagery, Inc.; used by permission.)

Figure 6. Oblique aerial photograph taken in April 1989. The base of this failure was located near the top of the thin-bedded unit shown in Figure 5 and primarily involved terrace sands. Most of the debris was deposited on the talus apron below the elevation of the basal slip surface. (Copyright Geo Tech Imagery, Inc.; used by permission.)

Figure 7. Oblique aerial photograph taken on January 20, 1993. This failure occurred on an out-of-slope bedding plane at the base of the marine terrace sands. Fluid flow of the terrace deposits resulted in approximately 4.6 m (15 ft) of bluff-top retreat. (Copyright Geo Tech Imagery, Inc.; used by permission.)

Figure 8. Oblique aerial photograph taken on February 25, 1993. The third bluff-top house from right was cut in half with chain saw by the owner prior to the failure. Note seepage along bedding to the left of the landslide. (Copyright Geo Tech Imagery, Inc.; used by permission.)

Figure 9. Soldier-pile and lagging wall installed to provide access for the railroad. (Photograph by authors.)

ing the period between 1850 and 1870 (Zeiser Geotechnical, 1990), suggesting that warmer water was present at that time. These observations seem similar to the periodic effects of what are known as El Niño conditions today.

Tremendous storms during the winter of 1861–1862 had an impact on the southern California area (Kuhn and Shepard, 1984). Excessive rainfall (259 cm [102 in]) was reported during this time in central California, and the entire San Joaquin Valley in central California and the Mission Valley in San Diego were reportedly flooded.

In 1884, 203 cm (80 in) of rainfall was recorded in the San Diego back country (Kuhn and Shepard, 1984). In 1891, 29 cm (11.5 in) of rain fell in an 8-hr period in Campo near the Mexican border. The Los Angeles River changed course during this storm period.

In 1939, waves as high as 12.5 m (40 ft) were reported in the San Pedro and Long Beach areas (Horrer, 1950). A groundswell of 13.7 m (45 ft) was recorded in the Catalina Channel (Marine Advisers, 1960), and eyewitnesses in the Dana Point area reported that storm waves 7.3 m (24 ft) in height inundated the Capistrano Beach area, covering PCH and attacking the base of the coastal bluffs at the La Ventana site.

Between 1947 and 1977, fewer major storms were recorded. Major beach-front and bluff-top urbanization occurred. A return to more stormy conditions began with the rains of 1969 and 1978, which caused significant damage in coastal communities (Zeiser Geotechnical, 1990). Widespread coastal damage also occurred during the 1982–1983 storms.

During the 1992–1993 season, over 53.3 cm (21 in) of rain fell in the Capistrano Beach area. Although this total accumulation was not record breaking, the single-month peak in January 1993 of 29.0 cm (11.4 in) was the highest in the last 30 yr (Fig. 10). This intense rainfall triggered the La Ventana landslide.

FIELD INVESTIGATION

The initial phase of field investigation began on February 26, 1993, and consisted of four 732-cm (24-in)-diameter bucket-auger

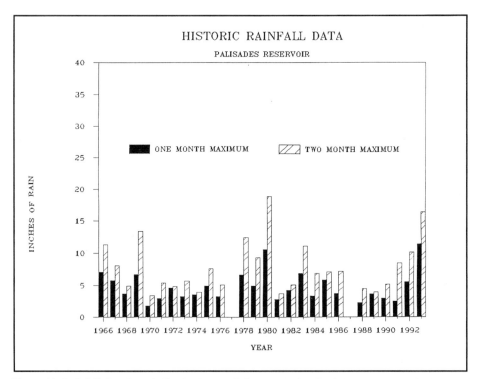

Figure 10. Rainfall data from Palisades Reservoir in Dana Point. Dark bars represent single-month maximum rainfall for the year.

borings excavated in La Ventana Street adjacent to the head scarp of the La Ventana landslide (Figs. 11 and 12). Borings ranged in depth from 19.8 to 30.5 m (65 to 100 ft). Three additional bucket-auger borings, ranging from 15.2 to 19.2 m (50 to 63 ft) in depth, were excavated in the upper part of the landslide. The borings extended to a depth below the prelandslide base of the bluffs. The authors were lowered into these borings in order to geologically log the exposed conditions. Representative bulk bag and relatively undisturbed core samples of terrace deposits, bedrock, and the basal slide gouge were collected for laboratory testing. Two additional small-diameter borings were excavated near the base of the bluff in PCH.

Slope inclinometer casing was installed in three of the four borings (LB-1, 2, and 4) in La Ventana Street adjacent to the landslide head scarp. All other borings were backfilled and compacted with the excavated native materials. Limited monitoring with a slope inclinometer probe from March 3 through May 10, 1993, indicated no significant ground movement at these three locations.

Several trenches were excavated with a track-mounted backhoe along the landslide margins, in the toe area and in the talus deposits adjacent to the slide. Detailed geologic mapping within the slide area was performed jointly by the authors. Several traverses up the bluff were mapped southeast of the slide to Camino Capistrano and along a stretch of bluff ~305 m (1,000 ft) northwest of the landslide. The topographic base maps depicting the prefailure and postfailure conditions (Gabel, Cook and Beckland, Inc., 1993) were utilized as topographic base maps (Figs. 11 and 12) for our investigation.

Crack displacement monitors were installed across cracks at strategic locations adjacent to the landslide headscarp. Data collected from February 26 through May 13, 1993, indicated that the maximum movement indicated by the monitors amounted to <2 mm (0.08 in). No significant pattern of crack expansion or

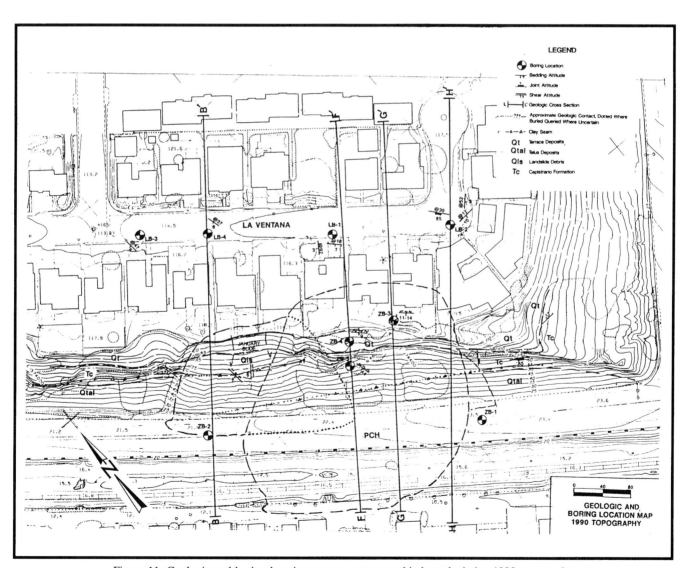

Figure 11. Geologic and boring location map on a topographic base depicting 1990 topography. Selected cross-section lines have been eliminated for clarity.

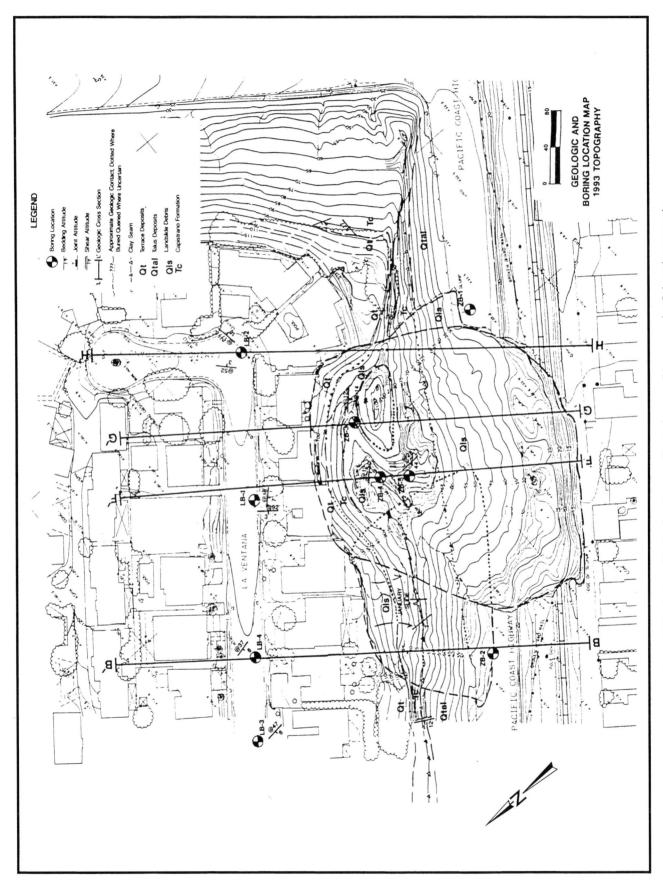

Figure 12. Geologic and boring location map illustrating postslide topography. Selected cross-section lines have been eliminated for clarity.

propagation was observed during the implementation of this program except as discussed in the summary of stability analysis section of this chapter.

GEOLOGIC CONDITIONS

Geologic setting

The site is located within the northwestern corner of the Peninsular Range geomorphic province of southern California near the western foothills of the Santa Ana Mountains. The bluffs are composed of Capistrano Formation (Tc) with a 6-m (20±-ft) thick veneer of marine terrace (Qtm) and nonmarine terrace deposits (Qtn) capping the bluff-top area. The Capistrano Formation, a marine siltstone of upper Miocene to lower Pliocene age, was deposited in a relatively narrow marine trough known as the Capistrano Embayment and extends in roughly a north-south direction. During late Pliocene to early Pleistocene time, the southern Orange County coastline was tectonically uplifted and emerged from the sea. Numerous wave-cut platforms were formed as the sea receded. Most of the wave-cut surfaces were covered by thin marine terrace deposits. Erosion from the adjacent highlands produced a nonmarine sedimentary cover over the marine terrace deposits.

Stratigraphy

The bluff stratigraphy consists of landslide debris, fill, beach sand, talus, terrace deposits, and siltstone bedrock (Capistrano Formation). These units and their relationships are discussed in detail below.

Landslide debris (Qls) consists of two contrasting material types: (1) saturated fine to coarse sands, silts, and clays derived from the marine and nonmarine terrace deposits, and (2) large blocks of unoxidized siltstone. Debris from the rear yards (i.e., patio furniture, potted plants, etc.) was strewn over the middle to lower surface of the landslide. The graben area was filled with crushed house parts, furniture, and kitchen appliances mixed with terrace deposit material (Fig. 13).

Artificial fill (Af) was encountered in small volumes associated with bluff-top grading and improvements. Minor volumes of fill were observed under the remaining portions of several residences in the headscarp area, ranging from a few centimeters to 0.9 m (3 ft) thick. The fill consisted of a mixture of sand, silt, and clay in thin horizontal lifts. The base of the fill was in sharp contact with nonmarine terrace deposits and locally with colluvium occupying old gullies. Fill exposed in the headscarp directly beneath the remaining parts of the homes appeared to be relatively dry. Subdrains were not observed beneath the exposed fill.

Beach sand (Qb) was encountered in Boring ZB-2 located on PCH and is essentially as shown in Figure 14. This material consisted of light brown, moist to wet, medium dense, silty fine sand. The sand interfingers with the talus deposits.

Talus deposits (Qtal) consist of a loose chaotic mixture of topsoil, terrace deposits, and platy to blocky fragments of siltstone,

Figure 13. View on February 27, 1993, looking southeast of landslide headscarp, graben area, and upper slide block. (Photograph by authors.)

which was relatively dry at the time of exploration. The base of this unit is roughly at the elevation of PCH, and the upper limits of talus deposits range from 9.1 to 18.3 m (30 to 60 ft) above the highway (Fig. 12).

Nonmarine terrace deposits (Qtn) consist of light brown silty clays, clayey silts, silty sands, and clayey fine sands ranging in thickness from 3 to 4.3 m (10 to 14 ft). The upper 0.9 to 1.5 m (3 to 5 ft) of this unit was very moist to saturated in the borings. Samples tested for moisture content at a depth of 1.5 m (5 ft) in each boring ranged from 87 to 98% saturated. Minor seepage occurred in the upper 1.2 m (4 ft) of this unit in Borings LB-1, LB-2, and LB-3.

Paleosols were observed within the nonmarine terrace deposits in borings beneath La Ventana Street and during mapping in the headscarp area. They are moderately porous, with manganese oxide lining pore holes, and relatively flat but not laterally continuous. The paleosols exposed in Borings LB-2 and LB-4 consisted of dark brown organic-rich clay with scattered fragments of charcoal. These old soil horizons were ~1.25 to 2.5 cm (0.5 to 1 in) thick.

Nonmarine terrace deposits exposed in the bluff are up to 6.1 m (20 ft) thick and exhibited similar contact relationship with the underlying marine terrace as observed in borings. Krotovina were encountered in the headscarp 0.3 to 0.9 m (1 to 3 ft) below the ground surface. The basal contact with the underlying marine terrace was sharp.

Marine terrace deposits (Qtm), ranging in thickness from 1.2 to 2.4 m (4 to 8 ft), consist of light brown, moist, dense, fine- to medium-grained sand with occasional cobbles. A concentrated zone of cross-bedding occurs in the lower 1 m (3 ft). Orange and gray to black, medium- to coarse-grained sand beds ~2.5 cm (1 in) thick occur at the base of this unit. The black color of the sand is most likely due to manganese oxide precipitating from migrating groundwater. Minor seepage was observed at the terrace-bedrock contact in all borings except LB-2. The contact with the Capistrano Formation below is very sharp, but irregular, and at an angle that varied from 2 to 7° to the southwest. Correlating this

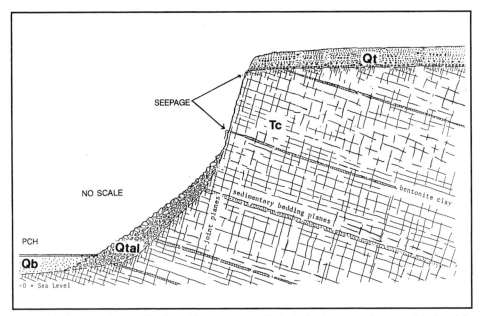

Figure 14. Cartoon of typical bluff profile and structure in the Palisades area. Dip reversal in the vicinity of the La Ventana landslide is anomalous. (Modified from R and M Consultants, Inc., 1982.)

contact from the bluff face to the borings resulted in an overall dip angle of approximately 3° to the southwest.

The marine terrace deposits thicken toward the bluff face and toward the south end of La Ventana Street. Channels with relief of 0.3 to 0.6 m (1 to 2 ft) and filled with rounded gravel were observed locally in the headscarp area. Minor seepage was observed flowing from a channel below Lot 27.

The unconformable contact between the marine terrace deposits and the Capistrano Formation is consistent throughout the Capistrano Beach area. The contact consistently dips toward the bluff face.

Two distinct units within the Capistrano Formation siltstone are present at the site. The lower unit is generally massive, whereas the upper unit is thin bedded. The primary (lower) unit consists of dark gray to black, clayey to fine sandy siltstone. On drier, weathered, and oxidized bluff-face outcrops, this unit exhibited a light gray color and closely spaced near-vertical jointing. The siltstone is generally massive to poorly bedded, micaceous, moist, and stiff with a petroliferous odor. Locally, bedding consists of thin lenses and stringers of white very fine sand and horizons of mica alignment. Some thin clay interbeds were observed in the borings. In La Ventana Street and in the headscarp area, the upper 0.3 to 1.2 m (1 to 4 ft) of this unit were weathered to a medium gray color, with orange iron staining along joints. The transition to the dark gray unoxidized siltstone was fairly sharp in all borings and in exposures in the headscarp area. A 7.6- to 20.3-cm (3- to 8-in)-thick zone directly below the terrace-bedrock contact exhibited a significantly higher clay content, probably as a result of interaction with migrating perched water. This occurs in an area where the upper unit pinches out, resulting in terrace deposits in direct contact with the lower unit. Shearing was observed at the base of the clayey

zone. Discrete isolated concretions were exposed on the bluff face. Talus derived from this siltstone unit generally consists of small irregularly-shaped fragments and loose silt.

Although not observed in the borings excavated on La Ventana Street, several large blocks of displaced siltstone from the lower unit were found within the slide debris with coatings of tan, wet, fat, extremely plastic sheared clay, where blocks had broken along bedding.

The upper bedrock unit consists of a thin bedded to laminated sequence of dark gray, diatomaceous siltstones, interbedded with white, very fine sandstone and medium gray clay. In bluff outcrops, this unit is characterized by a light gray color and well-developed, thin to very thin bedding with closely spaced near-vertical joints. A very thin sheared clay bed separates the upper unit from the lower unit. This sheared clay was mapped in the bluff north of the landslide. When encountered in borings on La Ventana Street, the upper unit had a very distinct hydrogen sulfide odor. Cemented zones within the upper unit correlate between the borings on La Ventana Street and the bluff/headscarp exposures. Gypsum crystals and iron stains line fracture surfaces and bedding planes where this unit crops out in the bluff northwest of the landslide. The unit thickens to the north and pinches out at the unconformable terrace-bedrock contact in the vicinity of Lot 25 and in Borings LB-1 and LB-2. The laminated siltstone tends to spall upon weathering at the surface, producing platy fragments.

Detailed stratigraphic analysis allowed the correlation of the data obtained in the borings to the exposures in the bluff face. This enabled an accurate recreation of the geologic condition in the bluff prior to failure, which aided in back-calculation analysis for shear strength. Also, it provided for an assessment of slope stability conditions for the property adjacent to the headscarp of the landslide.

Structure

The bedrock in the Capistrano Beach area consists of a homoclinal sequence of layered sedimentary strata that generally dip to the northeast, into the bluff face. Near-vertical joint sets are the predominant feature controlling bluff morphology (Fig. 14). The dominant jointing within the bedrock exposed in the bluff face consists of two preferred-orientation sets. One is roughly parallel to the bluff, dipping 50 to 85° to the southwest, and the other is perpendicular to the bluff, dipping 75° in either direction to vertical. Jointing observed in borings was more variable; however, the dominant joint set strikes roughly north-south and dips 55° to the west. Joints in the bluffs have been observed to be open up to 1 m (3.3 ft) prior to block topple failures that are typical of the area. Joint density and width tend to increase with proximity to the bluff face because of the stress field near the free face.

An anticline oriented roughly perpendicular to the bluff face is present southwest of Lot 25. Bedding is well defined by a thin lens of laminated siltstone exposed just below the terrace bedrock contact on the northwest limb of the fold. Bedding on the southeast limb is not as well defined within the massive siltstone unit.

Warping of strata in the immediate vicinity of the landslide area has resulted in the dipping of beds to the northwest, obliquely toward the slope face (Fig. 15). Bedding dip angles decrease with depth in the vicinity of the landslide. In the upper part of the bluff, bedding dips obliquely toward the bluff face between 7 and 14°. At the base of the bluff, bedding is essentially horizontal.

Bedding within the upper unit of the Capistrano Formation adjacent to Lots 25 and 26 is locally highly contorted by soft-sediment deformation (Fig. 16). Flattening of bedding dips at depth appears to be related to depositional conditions rather than postdepositional folding or faulting.

Adverse bedding conditions (bedding inclined toward the bluff face) are present beneath properties adjacent to the La Ventana Landslide (Figs. 12 and 15). Immediately south of the landslide, out-of-slope dipping shear surfaces along bedding indicated some movement had occurred within the remaining portion of the bluff. Siltstone above the shear surface overhangs the bedrock immediately below by several centimeters. Stria on the shear surface in this area indicate movement perpendicular to the bluff face. Slippage in the area immediately adjacent to the southerly flank of the slide mass appears to have stopped after several centimeters of movement. This potential failure zone was mitigated during the final bluff repair.

Bedding, sheared zones, and clay interbeds present immediately north of the landslide mass remain inclined obliquely toward the bluff face with an out-of-slope dip component of 4 to 8°.

SUBSURFACE WATER

Perched subsurface water was encountered at different elevations during this investigation. The shallowest occurrence of seepage was from the upper 1.2 m (4 ft) of the nonmarine terrace below La Ventana Street.

Subsurface water primarily occurs at the terrace-bedrock contact. The base of the terrace deposits consists of highly friable, uncemented sand with high permeability. The siltstone bedrock tends to act as an aqautard. In Borings LB-1, LB-3, and LB-4, minor seepage flowed from the base of the terrace sands. Seepage along the terrace-bedrock contact was not observed in Boring LB-2, although the basal sands were wet. Seepage along the contact at the bluff face occurs as a sharp, narrow subhorizontal zone.

Although water can migrate down through fractures, joints, and permeable layers in the bedrock, no groundwater was observed along the closed and discontinuous fractures/joints observed in the borings excavated in the bedrock during this investigation. The only exception was in Boring ZB-5 drilled through the slide mass at the previous bluff face. In Boring ZB-5, moderate seepage flowed from joints below the basal rupture surface of the landslide.

Minor seepage was observed in Borings ZB-3 through ZB-5 from just above the basal rupture surface of the landslide.

Evidence of past localized seepage on the bluff face in the immediate vicinity of the landslide is well documented through numerous historic photographs and other sources. Seepage zones visible in the 1979 oblique air photographs (Fig. 5) include a near horizontal zone at the base of the marine terrace deposits and two additional zones within the bedrock on the bluff face. One is located at the sheared clay contact between the upper and lower siltstone units, and the second coincides with a thin sand-over-clay bedding sequence within the lower unit. A limited exposure of the lower seepage zone was mapped in the bluff face south of the landslide.

MASS MOVEMENT AND FAILURE MECHANISM

The La Ventana landslide failed by translational block-glide movement along a weak clay bed dipping out-of-slope within the siltstone bedrock, accompanied by debris fall of the majority of the slide mass. The first manifestation of the main slide consisted of tension cracking in the headscarp area and continuous talus accumulation after the minor landslide in mid-January. Development of the headscarp along preexisting high-angle jointing began four to five days before the catastrophic movement of the landslide. The landslide moved obliquely to the bluff face. This conclusion is supported by (1) the topographic base map depicting the postlandslide conditions (Fig. 3), (2) an oblique aerial photograph taken on February 25, 1993, that reveals the same sense of movement (Fig. 8), and (3) the presence of major pieces of house debris in the slide mass, which could be correlated with the former residences.

The landslide buried portions of PCH, the railroad, and Beach Road. Individual concrete K-rails were pushed out from the northeast side of PCH to the railroad track area. The steel guard rail on the southwest side of PCH was detached and pushed out to the toe of the slide. The maximum thickness of slide material on PCH was ~10.7 m (35 ft). The runout distance for the slide was ~67 m (220 ft).

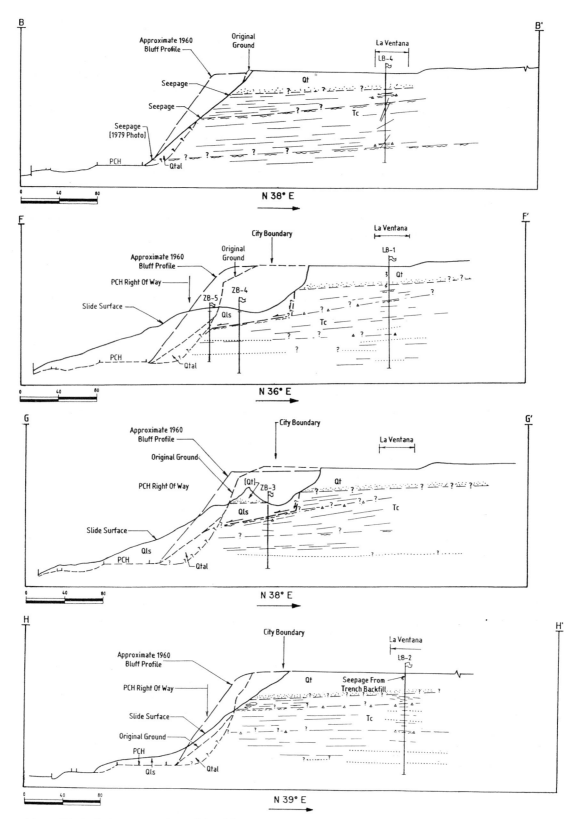

Figure 15. Geologic cross sections of the slide area. "Original ground" (short dashed line) approximates topography immediately prior to the January failure. Solid line represents postslide conditions. Cross section locations are indicated on Figures 11 and 12.

Figure 16. Tight folds sandwiched between planar bedding on the bluff face adjacent to slide below Lot 25. Horizontal span of photograph is ~2 m (7 ft). (Photograph by authors.)

The upper landslide block had a maximum thickness of 12.2 m (40 ft). During mapping of the slide mass the terrace-bedrock contact was exposed around this translated block. This contact proved to be useful in modeling movement of the slide block from its original position.

Three borings drilled within the landslide mass penetrated the rupture surface (Figs. 12 and 17). Borings ZB-3 and ZB-4 penetrated the basal rupture surface 4 m (12 ft) below the surface of the slide mass. The rupture surface in this area dipped 11 to 14° to the southwest. Boring ZB-5, excavated near the former position of the bluff face, pierced the slide in an area where the failure surface was controlled by joints dipping southwest at about 45°.

The joint-controlled headscarp within the bedrock dipped 80 to 88° southwest and was consistent with bluff-face joint orientation. The upper 3 to 4.6 m (10 to 15 ft) of headscarp within the terrace deposits was formed by slumping and sloughing. The old colluvium-filled gullies depicted on the original grading plan (Ayer, 1960) were exposed within the terrace deposits beneath a thin layer of artificial fill just below the building pad.

The landslide failed on out-of-slope bedding at approximately mid-bluff. Although the geologic structure provided the potential for failure, the probable occurrence of high positive pore-water pressures triggered the failure. Water saturated the basal claystone bedding, resulting in a loss of shear strength along the rupture surface; added weight to the overlying rock; and increased hydrostatic pressure within existing joints and bedding planes. The rains of January 1993, added to the existing subsurface water, were finally able to reduce the resisting forces holding the bluff in place.

SLOPE STABILITY CALCULATIONS

The purpose of slope stability analysis during the initial characterization of the landslide was to provide preliminary recommendations for design alternatives for stabilization of the La

Figure 17. View on April 5, 1993, looking south of bucket auger drilling/logging operation in graben area of landslide. (Photograph by authors.)

Ventana landslide and the reopening of PCH. Stability of existing improvements surrounding the slide area, including La Ventana Street and the remaining residences or parts of structures thereon, was also considered.

A simple model based on the prelandslide geometry was used to back-calculate the soil strength parameters. Additional strength parameters were determined by residual direct shear testing.

Slope stability was evaluated using the computer program PCSTABL5M, developed at Purdue University. PCSTABL5M performs two-dimensional slope stability analyses using various methods of slices. For our purposes, Modified Janbu's method was utilized, which provides for specification of an irregular noncircular slip surface. Hydrostatic forces were included in the analysis.

Laboratory Testing

Laboratory testing was conducted on samples from highly sheared plastic clays, bedrock, and terrace deposits. Laboratory tests included determination of residual shear strength, Atterberg

limits, grain-size analysis, and in situ moisture and density determination. Laboratory data are presented in Table 1.

Residual shear tests are intended to obtain the ultimate or
residual strength that remains in clay after having been subjected to
a large shearing strain under drained conditions. Residual strength
data were used in stability calculations.

Atterberg limits are used to delineate the moisture content
at arbitrarily defined boundaries of soil states. These values have
also been correlated to other soil engineering properties such as
shear strength, compression, and expansion indices.

Selection of strength parameters

Strength parameters (c and Φ) were selected on the basis of
formational unit, material type, and failure mechanism. The decision of whether to use in-place, remolded, or residual shear values was made primarily on the basis of the failure mechanism
used in modeling the slope. Undisturbed samples of natural
materials were used to determine peak and residual strength.
Remolded sample values were used for modeling fill materials.
The joints, clay seams, and failure planes were assumed to have
exhibited prior movement and to have retained only their residual
strength characteristics. For the purpose of our analysis, the lowest tested shear strength parameters were utilized for slip surfaces. These tested values are consistent with the values obtained
by back-calculation of the prelandslide bluff profile and subsurface geometry.

Summary of stability analysis

The stability of the central portion of the headscarp area
(cross section F-F', Fig. 15) was found to be less than unity to a
point 13.7 m (45 ft) behind the headscarp. Behind this 13.7-m
(45-ft)-wide zone, the factor of safety was calculated at greater than
1.0 (Zeiser Kling Consultants, Inc., 1993b). A crack-monitoring
meter installed near the 13.7-m (45-ft) demarcation line showed
~2 cm (0.8 in) of separation between May and October 1993, indicating that the stability calculations were valid and realistic. An
evaluation of stability of La Ventana Street at the same location
resulted in an average factor of safety of 1.1 (Leighton and Associates, Inc., 1993), consistent with the evaluation by Zeiser Kling in
the same area.

The factors of safety for the intact bluff face and for La Ventana Street immediately north of the slide were calculated to be
0.87 and 2.57, respectively. The factors of safety for the intact
bluff face and for La Ventana Street immediately south of the
landslide were calculated to be 1.23 and 2.02, respectively.

TABLE 1. LABORATORY TEST RESULTS

DIRECT SHEAR TESTS		
Test Location	Friction Angle (Φ)	Cohesion (psf)
LB-2 @ 10' (Qt)	15	1,000
LB-2 @ 15' (Qt)	36	0
ZB-1 @ 25' (Tc)	34	2,100
ZB-2 @ 20' (Tc)	54	1,600
Qls #A*	27	850
Qls #B*	31	300
LB 3 @ 40	25	240
LB 4 @ 29	8.6	0
Clay Seam #1†	11	200
Clay Seam #2†	14	100

ATTERBERG LIMITS			
Sample	L.L. (%)	P.L. (%)	P.I. (%)
Clay Seam #1	120	35	85
Clay Seam #2	101	34	67

MAXIMUM DENSITY TESTS		
Test Location	Maximum Dry Density (pcf)	Optimum Moisture (%)
Qls Debris #A	106.0	17.0
Qls Debris #B	121.0	12.0

*Remolded to 90% Relative Compaction.
†Values utilized for basal rupture in stability calculations.

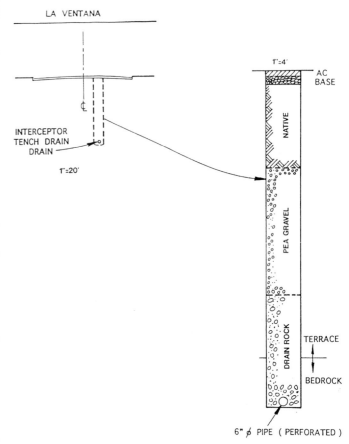

Figure 18. Cross-section diagram of groundwater interceptor drain
detail recommended for city of San Clemente. Drain would have exited
at Camino Capistrano.

MITIGATION ALTERNATIVES

Preliminary alternatives

For the city of San Clemente, design criteria stipulated that preliminary design recommendations for enhancement of stability of the La Ventana right-of-way be confined within their corporate boundaries. Preliminary mitigation recommendations consisted of installation of an interceptor trench drain along La Ventana Street to intercept the flow of subsurface water perched at the base of the terrace deposits and migrating toward the bluff zone (Fig. 18).

Additional recommendations included periodic property inspections for proper drainage, periodic leak detection of plumbing, consideration of choice of landscape plant type, regulated irrigation programs, and coordinated distress reporting systems.

Because of perceived seemingly insurmountable political issues, the city of Dana Point originally requested that preliminary design alternatives be provided that; (1) were entirely within the PCH right of way, (2) were entirely within the city corporate boundaries, and (3) ignored corporate boundaries (Fig. 19). Initially, the city of Dana Point requested that mitigation alternatives be based on grading rather than a hardface wall retained by rock bolt tie

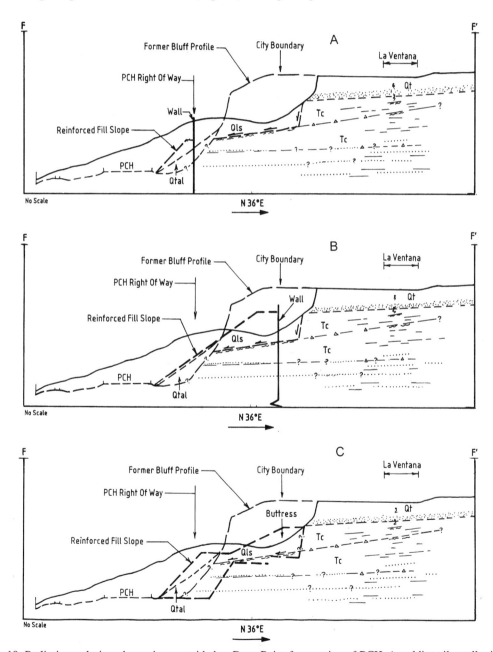

Figure 19. Preliminary design alternatives provided to Dana Point for opening of PCH. A, soldier-pile wall with reinforced fill slope within PCH right-of-way. B, soldier-pile wall and reinforced fill at corporate boundary. C, minimum buttress design height required to provide a factor of safety of 1.5. Note that the buttress would cross the city boundary.

backs. This stipulation was made because the city felt that mitigation might not have moved forward without the consent of, and indemnification by, the homeowners in San Clemente. Dana Point was essentially requesting that all the owners of bluff-top lots hold the city of Dana Point harmless for any additional damage that could occur during, or as a result of, implementation of repair work. Homeowners, wary of giving up their right to litigation, were initially reluctant to sign any type of waiver. The city, under pressure from federal agencies providing funding for design and repair work, was encouraged to provide a design that would at least provide the homeowners with a degree of enhanced stability that could be utilized for future residential reconstruction, but the city would not move forward without the waivers. Two of three preliminary design alternatives provided no benefit to bluff-top lots. The city was prepared to move forward with either one of these designs if the homeowners elected not to indemnify them. Bluff-top property owners therefore became motivated to sign waivers, which would allow the design and construction of a mitigation alternative within and beneath the limits of their respective properties. Mitigation not bounded by property lines or corporate boundaries would provide significant benefit to damaged property, allowing for ultimate reconstruction.

Preliminary remediation alternatives were based on the perceived worst-case condition, which assumed that failure would propagate on a projection of the basal rupture surface extending beneath the intact headscarp area (Fig. 19). Preliminary mitigation designs based on grading were then applied to cross sections and adjusted to establish a minimum factor of safety of 1.5.

Final design

The final design (Nolte and Associates, Inc., 1994) utilized a textured "hard-face" wall anchored by tie-backs extending below the rupture surface (Fig. 20). The area behind and above the wall was replaced with a compacted fill. A shallow interceptor drain was installed in La Ventana Street,

and a series of subdrains beneath the fill convey subsurface water to the bluff face.

CONCLUSIONS

The La Ventana landslide occurred shortly after the heaviest recorded single-month rainfall since the time of bluff-top urbanization. Because of adverse bedding conditions, the area was marginally stable even before the construction of the bluff-top residences. In addition to infiltration of rain water, other possible (although undocumented) sources for long-term buildup of subsurface water could include irrigation, leaking municipal or residential utilities, and water migrating through granular utility backfill. The structural condition responsible for the slide is limited in lateral extent and is localized in the immediate area of the failure. Bedding surfaces dipping out of the bluff became the basal surface of the landslide and are believed to be a result of an anomaly in the depositional environment, either fan progradation or soft sediment deformation. Uniform regional uplift relative to sea level and subsequent erosion exposed this anomaly on the bluff face. Because bedding flattens with depth, stability increases lower in the bluff. The head scarp was controlled by high-angle joints.

The areas on the flanks of the landslide are underlain by bedding that dips obliquely out-of-slope. However, bedding flattens and reverses dip as distance from the slide mass increases. The flanking areas were considered marginally stable prior to reconstruction, although the final design enhances stability. Additional failure of the unstable headscarp and flanking areas would likely have occurred had repair operations not been implemented.

The remainder of the bluffs will continue to retreat on a steady but sporadic basis as the result of joint-controlled block-topple–type failures. Inevitable continued bluff-top retreat adjacent to the repair area may result in future degradation of the hardface wall.

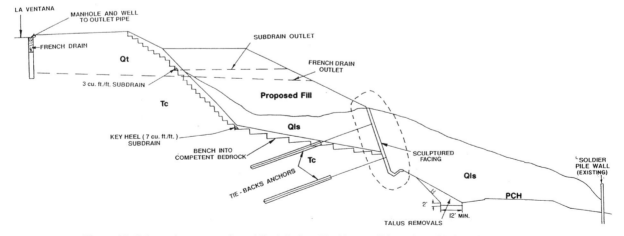

Figure 20. Schematic cross section of final design. Hardface wall is anchored below the rupture surface. Fill behind wall is benched into undisturbed siltstone or terrace deposits. Tie-backs enhance headscarp during construction and extend beyond slide limits to enhance stability of flanking areas to north and south. (After Nolte and Associates, 1994.)

ACKNOWLEDGMENTS

The information contained in this document is derived from reports prepared by the authors for the cities of Dana Point and San Clemente. These reports are public record and are on file at the respective cities. Support from NMG Geotechnical, Inc., and Zeiser-Kling Consultants, Inc., during the preparation of this document is appreciated. Woody Higden of Geo-Tech Imagery was very helpful in providing historical oblique aerial photographs of the area. The authors would like to thank the anonymous technical reviewers for their valuable input and Mr. Larson and Mr. Slosson for their technical review and editorial comments.

REFERENCES CITED

Ayer, W. A., 1960, 50-scale grading plan for Tract No. 3958, San Clemente, California, November 30, 1960. On file at the city of San Clemente.

Edgington, W. J., 1974, Geology of the Dana Point Quadrangle, Orange County, California: California Division of Mines and Geology Special Report 109, 31 p.; geologic map, scale 1:12,000.

Gabel, Cook and Beckland, Inc., 1993, Untitled 40-scale topographic base map covering the February 22, 1993, La Ventana landslide, March 2, 1993. On file at the city of Dana Point.

Horrer, P. L., 1950, Southern hemisphere swell and waves from a tropical storm at Long Beach, California: Scripps Institution of Oceanography, Publication Contribution 475, 18 p. Report from Beach Erosion Bulletin v. 4, July 1, 1950.

Kuhn, G., and Shepard, F. P., 1984, Sea cliffs, beaches and coastal valleys of San Diego County; some amazing histories and horrifying implication: Berkeley, University of California Press, 193 p.

Leighton and Associates, Inc., 1993, Impact of La Ventana landslide on the stability of La Ventana Street right-of-way, San Clemente, California, Project No. 1930152-01, prepared for the city of San Clemente, May 26, 1993.

Marine Advisers, 1960, Design waves for proposed small craft harbor at Oceanside, California, prepared for U.S. Army Engineers District, Los Angeles.

Nolte and Associates, Inc., 1994, City of Dana Point, California, Coast Highway landslide remediation and slope reconstruction construction documents, ER-2457(001), Job Number 3080-94-21, 15 sheets, prepared for city of Dana Point, May 5, 1994.

R and M Consultants, Inc., 1982, Engineering geology study of the Capistrano Beach Area, County of Orange, California, prepared for the Orange County Environmental Management Agency, Planning Division, Project No. 171103, May 24, 1982.

Rattray and Associates, Inc., 1990, Untitled 40-scale topographic base map covering a 750-foot section of La Ventana and adjacent bluff, prepared for city of Dana Point.

Walker, Doris, 1989, Orange County: A centennial celebration 1889–1989: n.p., Pioneer Publications.

Zeiser Geotechnical, Inc., 1990, Cotton/Beland Associates, Inc., City of Dana Point general plan, coastal erosion report, Project No. 89312-02, prepared for city of Dana Point, July 11, 1990.

Zeiser Kling Consultants, Inc., 1993a, Evaluation of La Ventana bluff failure located approximately 400 to 620 ft north of the intersection of Coast Highway and Camino Capistrano, Dana Point, California, Project No. 93121-00, prepared for city of Dana Point, February 22, 1993.

Zeiser Kling Consultants, Inc., 1993b, Geotechnical investigation with preliminary mitigation alternatives for the re-opening of Coast Highway, La Ventana bluff failure, Dana Point, California, Project No. 93121-01, prepared for city of Dana Point, April 30, 1994.

MANUSCRIPT ACCEPTED BY THE SOCIETY JANUARY 29, 1997

Index

[Italic page numbers indicate major references]